PRENTICE-HALL FOUNDATIONS OF MODERN *Genetics* SERIES

Sigmund R. Suskind and Philip E. Hartman, Editors

* Published jointly in Prentice-Hall's *Developmental Biology Series*

AGRICULTURAL

GENETICS

S
494
B7

James L. Brewbaker
University of Hawaii

PRENTICE-HALL, INC.   Englewood Cliffs, New Jersey

FOUNDATIONS OF MODERN GENETICS SERIES

Agricultural Genetics
C-01877-P   C-01878-C

PRENTICE-HALL INTERNATIONAL, INC., *London*
PRENTICE-HALL OF AUSTRALIA, PTY., LTD., *Sydney*
PRENTICE-HALL OF CANADA, LTD., *Toronto*
PRENTICE-HALL OF INDIA (PRIVATE) LTD., *New Delhi*
PRENTICE-HALL OF JAPAN, INC., *Tokyo*
PRENTICE-HALL DE MEXICO, S.A., *Mexico City*

To a devoted plant breeder and
his understanding wife: my parents

Foundations of Modern *Genetics*

Genetic research is alive with excitement and revolutionary advances. Important to the development of science and to the evolution of social structure, genetic thought is widening its impact on many areas: immunology, protein chemistry, cellular physiology, developmental biology, medicine, agriculture, and industry.

So many partnerships and such rapidly expanding methodology demand a fresh approach to genetic training —an approach attempted in this series.

The basic principles of genetics are few and simple. We present them with enough description of accessory scientific areas to allow comprehension not only of the principles themselves but also of the types of experiments from which the concepts have evolved. Such an approach compels the reader to ask: What is the *evidence* for this concept? What are its *limitations?* What are its *applications?*

The Prentice-Hall Foundations of Modern Genetics Series presents the evidence upon which *current* genetic thought is based. It is neither a history nor a survey of all genetic knowledge. The short volumes make possible a stimulating, selective treatment of the various aspects of genetics at the intermediate level, and sectional divisions allow free choice of emphasis in differently oriented college genetics courses.

The references cited in each volume and the current research literature are the immediate sequels to this series, but the true sequel remains in the hands of the alert reader. He will find here the seed of more than one enigma, the solution of which he, himself, may help bring into man's comprehension sometime in the future.

SIGMUND R. SUSKIND
PHILIP E. HARTMAN

McCollum-Pratt Institute
The Johns Hopkins University

Preface

Genetics assumes its most important role in relation to agriculture. Perhaps this will not be true in another century, as geneticists discover new applications for their knowledge in the fields of medicine and industry. So long as two-thirds of the world's people are undernourished, however, a fitting and challenging task for genetic research is that of discovering new ways to increase agricultural productivity and to improve the nutrition of man.

Some years ago, there existed a popular misimpression that anyone with full command of the genetics of a corn plant or a fruit fly could solve the problems of organisms such as bacteria, molds, and viruses by simple extrapolation. Today, the misimpression more often exists in reverse. In reality, however, genetic advance in agriculture rests almost entirely on genetic facts obtained from studies of cultigens, agriculturally important animals and plants. Most cultigens are complex higher organisms living in a complex environment. They hardly satisfy a scientist's yearning for "model systems."

The practical obstacles of space and finance lead the agricultural geneticist to make a judicious choice of genetic traits for his study. Only too often, these traits are governed by many genes, are greatly influenced by environment, and are difficult to measure—we may reflect, for example, on the problems of a geneticist studying prime rib production in beef cattle. The role of statistics in genetics is thus an integral one, and the biometrical material covered here should provide a solid background for advanced training in quantitative genetics.

Aspects of genetics that are particularly important in relation to agriculture include polygenic inheritance, genotype-environment interactions, hybrid vigor, host-parasite relationships, polyploidy, genetic lethals, genomic reconstruction, and the regulation of breeding systems. These areas will be explored thoroughly in the pages that follow, together with other aspects of genetic inquiry that provide a basis for advanced study into the creative arts of animal and plant breeding.

J.L.B.

Contents

xi

Biological Variation

Hard cash paid down, over and over again, is an excellent test of inherited superiority.[1]

Putting inherited superiority to work is a major objective of agricultural research. Well over half the people on our procreative earth have too little to eat, and even the most profound knowledge of the gene provides little comfort to empty stomachs until it is translated into calories. Genetics has paid its way in calories in the past by demonstrating that inherited superiority can be located, transferred, and used in many cultivated plants and domesticated animals. Among perhaps thirty thousand animals and plants that enter the world's commerce, however, comparatively few species have received the benefit of controlled genetic advances. Challenging frontiers for agricultural genetic research are provided by new species, as well as by new environments for crops and animals, new pests and diseases, new uses in biochemistry, and a spiraling world population.

Cultivated plants and domesticated animals are known as cultigens. With increasing precision, man is controlling both the genetics and environments of these cultigens. Agricultural genetics is defined by its relationship to them, just as medical genetics is defined by a relationship

[1] Charles Darwin, *Animals and Plants under Domestication* (Appleton, 1897), vol. I, p. 447.

1

to man. The most economically important cultigens are vertebrate animals and flowering plants, to which most of the illustrations and discussions that follow are related. Of course, the basic principles of genetics are the same for a cultigen as they are for a weed. As a matter of fact agricultural genetics often attains its objectives more rapidly through studies of viruses and weeds than it does through studies of cabbages or cows.

The genetics of cultigens is not the same as the breeding of cultigens. Animal and plant breeding involve many arts and sciences relating to cultigens, and genetics may be considered the most important of these. There are, of course, successful breeders who have little or no knowledge of the science of genetics. However, today's breeder has come to rely on some pretty sophisticated genetic methods, a fact that should become apparent in the pages that follow.

Describing biological variation

The description of biological variation is a starting point for any biological inquiry. The geneticist must distinguish the genetic from the nongenetic components of the variation if he is to discern the mode of inheritance of a trait being studied. It is to this partitioning of variability that much of our agricultural genetic inquiry must be directed. To this end, the science of genetics has come to use more and more complicated tools of the statistician. Nowhere is this more evident than in studies of the economically important characters of cultigens.

Two facts underlie the importance of statistics to agricultural genetics. In the first place, many economic traits are governed by many genes, and are continuous rather than discrete in their variation. Second, it is often necessary in agricultural research to derive genetic information with maximum efficiency from small populations. In studies of milk production or fruit color, for example, considerations of economy and time dictate that we get the most information out of the fewest possible cows or apple trees. No attempt will be made here to describe in detail the methodology of statistical or quantitative genetics, but the understanding of results derived from the statistical genetic approach will require the clear understanding of several basic constants and statistical concepts.

The statistics used to describe biological variation include measures of average, dispersion, and relationships. Among those most often used are:

Measures of average: Mean
Measures of dispersion: Variance, Range, Standard deviation
Measures of relationship: Correlation, Covariance

The two most important measures are mean and variance. The mean, symbolized by $\bar{x}$, describes the average or central tendency of a population; it is calculated by summing (Σ) the observations (X) and dividing by the number (n) of observations summed.

$$\bar{x} = \frac{\Sigma X}{n}$$

The dispersion of a population can be indicated most simply by its range, or extreme values. In many instances, a population's dispersion is as important as its mean. Consider, for example, two basketball teams:

Team A: 6'1", 6'2", 6'3", 6'4", 6'5"   Mean = 6'3"
Team B: 5'5", 5'6", 6'3", 7'0", 7'1"   Mean = 6'3"

Although these two teams have identical mean heights, the range of team B is five times that of team A. Given his choice of teams, then, a newcomer would probably elect to play with team B, with its towering seven-footers.

Of greater precision than the range in describing the dispersion of a population is the variance (V, or σ^2), the average of the squared deviations (d^2) of individual observations from the mean:

$$\sigma^2 = \frac{\Sigma d^2}{n - 1}$$

Note that we divide by $n - 1$ rather than by n; this is to adjust the variance of a sample of observations for their mean. We say that a single degree of freedom has been lost from n by this adjustment. For ease in machine calculations, variance is calculated directly from original measurements by use of the formula

$$\sigma^2 = \frac{\Sigma X^2 - (\Sigma X)^2/n}{n - 1}$$

The variance is the measure most frequently used in statistical genetics, since it is the most valuable of the statistics that describe the variation of a biological trait.

The square root of variance is the standard deviation (σ), which expresses dispersion in the same units of measurement as does the mean. When it is related directly to the mean in per cent, it forms a useful coefficient of variation.

$$\text{Coefficient of variation} = \frac{\sigma}{\bar{x}}$$

Coefficients of variation can be used to compare different experiments, since they are independent of units of measure. Coefficients of variation smaller than 10 per cent are uncommon in biological data.

For the basketball teams A and B, for example, variance values are

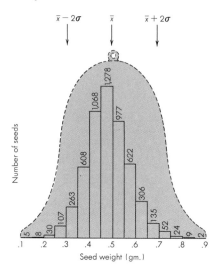

Fig. 1.1. **Normal probability distribution of 5,494 kidney bean seeds, grouped according to seed weight. Based on experiments of Wilhelm Johannsen.**

2.5 for team A and 90.5 for team B; standard deviations are 1.6 for team A and 9.4 for team B; and coefficients of variation are 2 per cent for team A and 13 per cent for team B. Each of these sets of values indicates the fact that the dispersion is much greater in team B than it is in team A.

The distribution of values about the mean for most biological characters assumes a characteristic bell-shaped pattern. This is illustrated in Fig. 1.1, which shows the weights of 5,494 kidney beans recorded by the great Danish geneticist Wilhelm Johannsen. The bell-shaped distribution can be duplicated by anyone willing to make 5,494 measurements of almost any biological trait. This type of distribution follows certain laws of probability and is known as the normal probability distribution. A normal distribution is symmetrical about the mean as midpoint, and 95 per cent of the population falls within the range from $\bar{x} - 2\sigma$ to $\bar{x} + 2\sigma$. In other words, values in a normal probability distribution exceed a deviation of 2σ, twice the standard deviation, less than 5 per cent of the time. The ratio of 95 per cent to 5 per cent, or of 19 : 1, is taken as safe betting-odds for much bioagricultural research. Thus, when values exceed a deviation of 2σ from the mean, the deviations are considered large enough to be significant, and the biologist may wisely seek a cause other than chance for the deviation. The normal probability distribution may be calculated empirically by expanding the binomial $(p + q)^n$, where n is infinitely large and $p = q$.

Measures of relationship include correlation and covariance. Each of these measures describes the change in one variable character as another one changes. Correlation is a measure of direct proportion. Thus, we say that height and weight of a growing animal are correlated, since when one of these variables increases, the other also increases. The weight of a mature Holstein cow may be used accurately to estimate the size of its heart, since these traits have the high correlation of 0.94 (100 per cent correlation = 1.0). In contrast, the milk production of a fat Holstein is not necessarily more than that of a skinny one, reflecting the rather poor correlation (0.35) of milk production and body girth. Covariance is a measure of correlation among two or more individuals or populations. The degree of resemblance between any two individuals or populations is to a large degree a function of the genes they have in common. Genetic covariance statistically expresses this resemblance in terms of variances. A high degree of covariance or correlation may indicate that one variable can be used accurately to predict changes in another.

Phenotypic variation

As has often been remarked, probably no two individuals are identically the same. All wild animals recognize each other, which shows that there is some difference between them; and when the eye is well practised, the shepherd knows each sheep, and man can distinguish a fellowman out of millions on millions of other men.[2]

Taken as a whole, the biological variation in any species is almost overwhelming. As Darwin noted, probably no two individuals (even "identical" twins) are wholly identical. Discrete genetic differences that bring hard cash to a rancher or farmer are usually quantitative and are often difficult to distinguish, measure, and evaluate. Discerning the heritable portion of this quantitative biological variation requires not only the "practised eye" (for which, however, there is no substitute) but also the best available statistical methods.

The total biological variation of a given trait is described statistically as its phenotypic variance (V_P). The components of phenotypic variance may be grouped into two major classes: genetic (V_G) and nongenetic or environmental (V_E). By definition, then,

$$V_P = V_G + V_E$$

The development of genetic laws has required the careful selection of traits in which V_E is minimized. Thus, Mendel reported in his published studies on peas that he was carefully avoiding phenotypes that showed "irregular or inconstant" variation. The thirty-four varieties of peas studied by Mendel segregated in many different characters, from which he chose only seven for his classic experiments. These seven characters, which were "constantly differentiating," were chosen because the phenotypic variation appeared to be largely genetic, with a

[2] Darwin, *Animals and Plants under Domestication*, vol. I, p. 361.

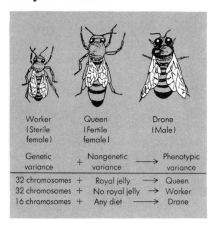

Worker (Sterile female)	Queen (Fertile female)	Drone (Male)

Genetic variance	+	Nongenetic variance	→	Phenotypic variance
32 chromosomes	+	Royal jelly	→	Queen
32 chromosomes	+	No royal jelly	→	Worker
16 chromosomes	+	Any diet	→	Drone

Fig. 1.2. Honeybees illustrate clearly that the genotype is only a set of potentialities upon which the environment must act to produce the phenotype we observe.

negligible nongenetic component. We may speculate that Mendel encountered greater nongenetic variation in mice and bees, which he studied in detail, but about which he never published his findings.

A detailed biochemical study of peas reveals immense variation that Mendel chose to overlook. A study of chlorophyll contents, for example, would reveal many degrees of seed color intermediate between Mendel's extremes of "pale yellow, bright yellow, and orange-colored" and "more or less intense green." It is perhaps fortunate that Mendel completed his experiments prior to this age of biochemical and statistical inquiry, else his F_2 ratio of 6,022 yellow and 2,001 green pea seeds might have been subdivided ad infinitum. At this point I encourage you to digress for thirty-seven minutes and read, if you have not done so recently, Mendel's classic paper "Experiments in Plant Hybridization." [3] These thirty-seven minutes will be among the best any student of genetics can spend, especially if he reflects while reading that the paper was written in 1865. He may also wryly meditate on the blind spots of Science, for this classic work evoked essentially no interest until its rediscovery and simultaneous substantiation in 1900 by Carl Correns, Erich von Tschermak, and Hugo de Vries.

Environmental variation

The living organism is constantly responding and adapting to its environment. In a broad sense, environment includes all intracellular and extracellular factors that influence the expression of the genotype. Any genetic description of a population of living plants or animals must, therefore, include observations (often quite detailed)

[3] Reprinted in *Classic Papers on Genetics*, J. A. Peters, ed. (Prentice-Hall, 1961), pp. 1-20.

about its environment, which are expressed in terms of environmental variance (V_E). V_E statistically incorporates all variation not directly attributable to segregating genes; hence it is often referred to as non-genetic variance.

The honeybee illustrates for us in a striking way the importance of nongenetic components in genetic analysis (see Fig. 1.2). The male bees (drones) arise from unfertilized eggs, irrespective of their diet during larval stages. The female bees (queens and workers) arise from fertilized eggs and vary greatly in their appearance, depending on their larval diet. The ability of so-called royal jelly to convert the female bee into a queen has been emphasized *ad nauseum*. It is perhaps more correct to consider the queen simply as a normal female, while the worker females are, in effect, starved queens who have been deprived of a decent diet. The workers have a short life span, are small in stature, and are usually incapable of laying eggs. Workers are thus impoverished expressions of their full genetic potentialities. The entire breeding and social structure of bees (and other insect species) therefore rests on the role of a nongenetic component, royal jelly, in the phenotypic expression of sex.

Environmental variance includes two major components, one intangible, the other controllable. Intangible variations include a statistical residue known as error and certain interactions of genetic and environmental components. Genetic experiments commonly are designed to minimize the variation from the controllable environmental component. Carried to practical extremes, this encourages the geneticist, for example, to produce germ-free chickens, to grow plants on nutrient agar, or to study microbes in nutritionally defined media.

Environmental variance can often be broken down so that the relative importance of controllable components can be assessed. Variance in the birth weights of mammals, for example, has been found to depend to a large degree on the environment, that is, on factors such as nutrition and health, of the mother. One analysis of phenotypic variance for human birth weights by L. S. Penrose gave the following results:

Source of variance	Per cent of variance attributable to source
Maternal environment	24
Maternal genotype	20
Age of mother	1
Numerical position of child	7
Intangible variations	30
Genotype of baby	18

The environment of the mother contributed more variance than did the baby's genotype in this study. Note that intangible variations contributed more than any other single component.

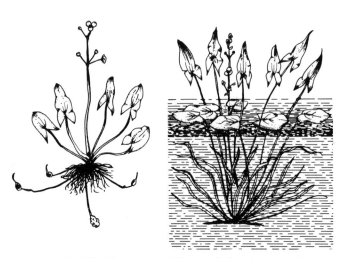
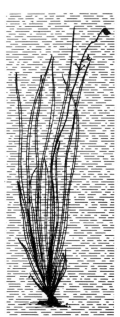

Fig. 1.3. The response of the arrowleaf to changes in its environment. Left, terrestrial growth; right, submersed growth; center, the arrowleaf as it is commonly found, partially submersed. From Bruce Wallace and Adrian M. Srb, *Adaptation*, 2nd ed. (Prentice-Hall, 1964), reproduced by permission of Prentice-Hall, Inc.

The environmental component of variance can be estimated most easily in studies of subjects or populations that have no genetic variance, such as identical twins or vegetative offspring of a single plant. In such studies, V_G equals zero, and V_P equals V_E. Populations with low genetic variance, such as highly inbred (pure) lines or the hybrids of two such lines, can also be effectively used. Caution must be exercised, however, lest the use of different, genetically uniform populations lead to different estimates of environmental variance. When tested under identical conditions, for example, corn hybrids show almost 30 per cent less environmental variance than do their inbred parents. This occurs in spite of the fact that their genetic components of variance are identical. Because of reasons explored in Chapter 5, inbreds interact more violently with environmental variations, while hybrids appear to be better "buffered" against these variations.

The adaptive responses of aquatic plants illustrate the unusual range of variations permitted by a single genotype in differing environments (see Fig. 1.3). Statistically, these variations in growth are entirely environmental; however, they reflect to a great extent the activity of certain genes in one environment and their inactivity or impaired activity in another. Environment acts as the "trigger" for the action of many genes of this type. Adaptive responses in segregating populations thus may reflect important interactions of genotype and environment. There are exceptions to every generalization, however, and studies have shown that some genotypes possess an unusual adaptability, thriving in many different environments. Plant and animal breeders have recognized this adaptability in certain breeds, such as Golden Cross Bantam corn and Holstein-Freisian cattle, and have prized them accordingly. It is clear that certain genes or genetic systems contribute directly to such adaptability.

Genetic variation and heritability

Genetic variation arises from the contribution of segregating genes and their interactions with other genes. The term *heritability* (*H*) expresses the proportion of the total phenotypic variance that is genetic:

$$H = \frac{V_G}{V_P} \quad \text{or} \quad \frac{V_G}{V_G + V_E}$$

This proportion is commonly expressed in percentages; heritability is equal to 100 per cent whenever there is no environmental variance. As the environmental component of variance increases, the heritability drops. Genetic advance through selection is the primary objective of animal and plant improvement. Effective selection of genetically superior individuals requires that two conditions be met: (1) phenotypic variation must be adequate in the original population and (2) heritability must be sufficiently high for effective selection. In general, as heritability and phenotypic variations increase, genetic advance through selection (see Chapter 9) also increases.

The carefully designed experiments of Wilhelm Johannsen—from which we inherit our terms *gene, genotype,* and *phenotype*—laid the foundation for the interpretation of genetic advance under selection with continuously varying characters. At the time of the rediscovery of Mendel's paper, it was considered highly improbable that such characters could be governed by genes at all. Sir Francis Galton's studies of height and other continuously varying characters in man had given great quantitative precision to the ideas of variation and inheritance proposed by his cousin Charles Darwin, but Galton was unable to distinguish clearly the genetic and nongenetic components of variation—simply because *Homo sapiens* provided unfavorable material for this study. Like Mendel, however, Johannsen made an unusually judicious selection of species for his study of the common kidney bean.

Johannsen observed that the kidney bean seeds from any one plant or variety varied greatly in weight. Starting with 5,494 seeds of a single variety, Johannsen determined the average seed weight to be 495 mg. When plotted, the individual seed weights had the bell-shaped normal distribution shown in Fig. 1.1. A few of the largest and smallest beans from this population were sown, and 19 plants were grown. The average weights of beans differed greatly among these 19 plants, ranging from a plant averaging 350 mg. per bean to a mammoth-seeded type averaging over 640 mg. per bean. When seeds were sown from the large-seeded plants, the offspring were similarly large seeded; offspring of the small-seeded forms were small seeded, etc. The 19 lines established from these original selections were grown for 6 generations.

By a simple but classic experiment, Johannsen showed that further selections in the 19 lines were not effective. To establish each of the 6 generations following his original selection, Johannsen planted a few of the largest and a few of the smallest beans from each line. (See Fig. 1.4, which shows data from one of the large-seeded selections.)

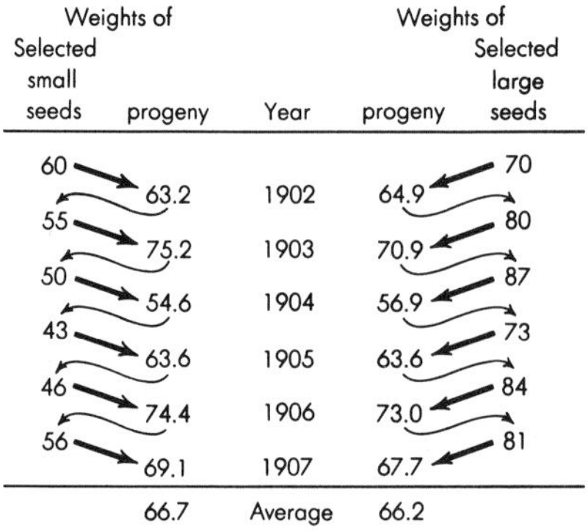

Weights of Selected small seeds	progeny	Year	progeny	Weights of Selected large seeds
60	63.2	1902	64.9	70
55	75.2	1903	70.9	80
50	54.6	1904	56.9	87
43	63.6	1905	63.6	73
46	74.4	1906	73.0	84
56	69.1	1907	67.7	81
	66.7	Average	66.2	

Fig. 1.4. The ineffectiveness of selection in a pure line, illustrated by bean seed weights in centigrams. Based on experiments of Wilhelm Johannsen.

With convincing regularity, the large and small sister seeds from any one line grew into plants having seeds of similar average weight. However, some variation in seed weight continued to occur each generation; Johannsen concluded that this variation was nongenetic. Note in Fig. 1.4 that the environmental variation from year to year was large, but affected large-seeded and small-seeded selections alike.

We can interpret Johannsen's results more easily knowing that kidney beans, like Mendel's peas, are regularly inbred by self-fertilization. *Continued inbreeding leads to genetic homozygosity.* The original kidney bean variety sampled by Johannsen was, in effect, a mixture of highly homozygous lines.[4] Selection of 19 seeds of different sizes had effectively separated this variety into 19 genotypically distinct lines. Self-fertilization led to no further genetic variability in the 19 lines, which Johannsen referred to as pure lines. We should not infer that

[4] It is customary to qualify the term *homozygous* when referring to the entire genotype; e.g., the "highly homozygous" line is one in which a great majority of the loci are homozygous.

these lines showed no variation, but rather, that measurable genetic variation (V_G) was absent and that $V_P = V_E$. Selection failed within the pure lines because no genetic variation for bean weights existed within them. Consider what might have happened had Johannsen chosen the highly cross-pollinated scarlet runner bean for his studies!

The three major components of genetic variance, originally proposed by Sewall Wright, are (1) additive genetic variance, (2) dominance deviation, and (3) interaction or epistatic deviation. Any two alleles that have differing quantitative effects contribute additive genetic variance. Whenever a heterozygote is more like one homozygote than the other, there arises a deviation from additive variance due to dominance. Genetic variances that involve alleles showing dominance include additive variance and deviations from additive variance caused by dominance. Epistasis and other nonallelic interactions also contribute deviation from additive genetic variance. We will return to these important concepts in the partitioning of genetic variance in Chapter 4.

Additive genetic variance is the chief cause of resemblance between relatives and is the main determinant of the responses of populations to selection. Whenever genetic variance can be partitioned, the additive component is used for precise estimates of heritability by the formula

$$\text{Coefficient of heritability} = \frac{V_A}{V_P}$$

The estimation of heritability coefficients was originally made by J. L. Lush from statistics that related the performance of a given animal to the performance of its offspring—in this case, for traits such as milk production. This relationship can be expressed in terms of covariance. The covariance of offspring with their parent (Cov_{OP}), as of calves with a common bull parent, directly estimates half the additive genetic variance of the trait being measured. This is expressed statistically as

$$Cov_{OP} = \frac{V_A}{2}$$

Heritability may then be expressed in terms of covariance as

$$H = \frac{2 \, Cov_{OP}}{V_P}$$

In a similar manner the covariances of animals related in other ways than parent and offspring may be used for calculation of V_A and heritability. The covariance method, however, does not provide accurate estimates of V_A and H whenever dominance or epistatic deviations are large.

The following coefficients illustrate the wide variation in heritabilities of economic traits.

5%	Conception rate in cattle
17%	Ear length in corn
20%	Egg production in *Drosophila*
20%	Egg production in poultry
25%	Yield in corn
30%	Milk production in cattle
40%	Fleece length in sheep
60%	Egg weight in poultry
65%	Root length in radishes
70%	Plant height in corn
85%	Slaughter weight in cattle

Many of these fall well below 50 per cent, indicating a more profound contribution from environment (and nonadditive genetic variance) than from additive genetic variance.

Putting genes to work

This first chapter has emphasized that the recognition and description of genetic components of variance is basic to all genetic inquiries. Specifically, however, agricultural genetic inquiries are most important insofar as they help to lay the foundation for putting genes to work. The following chapters relate to this thesis. The breeding systems of plants and animals (Chapter 2) determine to a great extent how genetic variation arises and how it can be used. Many economically important traits segregate into discontinuous classes, and most of these prove to be under relatively simple genetic control (Chapter 3). It is increasingly apparent, however, that most economically important traits display continuous or quantitative genetic variation that involves the action and interaction of many genes (Chapter 4). Heterosis or hybrid vigor (Chapter 5) has become the bread and butter for many animal and plant breeders. Polyploidy (Chapter 6) poses both problems and promises for genetic advance, and locating and putting mutations to work (Chapter 7) is a true frontier of agricultural genetic research. Parasitism and symbiosis (Chapter 8) present the geneticist with the challenge of two genetic systems interacting, often in very precise ways, together with some of the most important of the hard-cash problems of agricultural genetics. And, finally, genetic advance through selection (Chapter 9) is the tool that shapes the future.

The rapidly increasing populations of man, the continuing evolution of pests and diseases, the loss of rich farmlands, the challenges of converting strange new environments into economic use, even the challenge of satisfying the increased gastronomic curiosity of man—all present new frontiers to agricultural genetics. The following chapters deal with sources of genetic variance and the means of putting them to work that serve as foundations for much agricultural improvement. In this age of man's apparently unlimited ability to solve the riddles of nature, agricultural geneticists emphasize the importance of research with this sort of ultimate practicality.

References

Bates, Marston, *Man in Nature*. Englewood Cliffs, N.J.: Prentice-Hall, Inc. 1959. Chapters 6 and 7 provide an interesting backdrop for your study of genetics in agriculture.

Darwin, Charles, *Animals and Plants under Domestication*. New York: D. Appleton & Company, 1897. Classic studies of biological variation.

Peters, J. A., ed., *Classic Papers in Genetics*. Englewood Cliffs, N.J.: Prentice-Hall, Inc., 1961. See especially the papers of Mendel and Johannsen.

Problems

1.1. Two varieties of the long Japanese radish, Daikon, were grown in experiments at Misima, and the following root lengths in cm. obtained:

> Moriguti: 70, 90, 65, 75, 115, 100, 85, 80, 90, 65
> Minowase: 70, 45, 80, 65, 50, 50, 65, 55, 75, 50

Calculate the means and coefficients of variation for the two varieties.

1.2. When the radish variety Moriguti was grown in sandy soils at Gihu, roots averaged 102 cm. in length. Does this fall outside the range of $\bar{x} \pm 2\sigma$ that can be calculated from data in Problem 1.1? Would you take 19:1 odds that the growers in Gihu can always grow longer Moriguti radishes than growers in Misima?

1.3. V_P for radish root lengths is about 50. $V_E = 12$. What is the approximate heritability of this trait? More precise quantitative studies revealed that $V_A = 30$ for this trait. Calculate the true coefficient of heritability. What types of variance contribute to the differences between these heritability values?

1.4. The birth weights of baby pigs and the root lengths of radishes have comparable coefficients of variation. The covariance of baby pigs with their parents is 0.06, and their average weight is 3 pounds. Calculate the coefficient of heritability for birth weights of pigs.

Breeding Systems

To a great extent, the heritable variation we find about us results from the segregation and recombination of genes. In most living organisms, new variation arising from mutation is completely overshadowed by variation arising from recombination. Breeding systems, in the broad sense, include all factors that control the rate of release of genetic variation.

Complete genetic constancy is a luxury that few organisms have been able to afford. An occasional weed or parasite, however, finds an environmental niche and, with the help of genetic constancy, clings happily to it. One vigorous but self-incompatible (and hence genetically seedless) plant of the weedy *Veronica filiformis,* for example, spread successfully throughout Europe by vegetative reproduction alone. In even more dramatic fashion, new races of certain fungi ("imperfecti") that have no sexual reproduction at all evolve only through mutation. Thus a score of mutant races of the wilt fungus *Fusarium oxysporum* have extended the range of this severe disease to host plants as unrelated as bananas, cabbages, and flax. These and other examples stand out, however, as minor exceptions to the rule that genetic recombination through sexual reproduction is a major building-block in evolution.

14

Sex

Segregation and recombination in all important cultigens is a result of sexual reproduction involving the alternation of two generations, the diploid organism and the haploid sex cells. Most organisms that reproduce asexually are noncellular or unicellular haploid parasites, among whose large populations the rare mutations apparently suffice for adaptation and evolution. Genetic recombination, however, occurs sporadically in many, if not most, unicellular organisms following a mating process known as conjugation. Bacteria, viruses, algae, and fungi may be used to illustrate all three steps in the evolution of sexual reproduction: (1) the biochemical differentiation of mating types, (2) the morphological distinction of sex cells or gametes, and (3) the differentiation of organs for the exclusive production of male and female gametes, the sperm and the egg.

Most domesticated animals are unisexual, most cultivated plants bisexual. In unisexual or dioecious (literally, "two houses") organisms, the eggs are produced by one type of individual and the sperm by another. In bisexual organisms, both male and female organs are produced by the same individual. Plants like corn, in which the male and female parts are confined in separate flowers, are termed monoecious. Plants having male and female parts in the same flower are said to be hermaphrodites (Hermaphroditus, the son of Hermes and Aphrodite, became fused with a nymph while bathing). The term *hermaphrodite* is also applied loosely to all bisexual animals.

Bisexual animals include a large assortment of invertebrates, among them the sponges, the earthworms, and the well-studied coelenterate *Hydra*. These animals produce both eggs and sperm and, like the corn plant, are able to reproduce by self-fertilization. In contrast, bisexual animals occur very infrequently among the vertebrates. A rare example was the chicken that began its sexual life by laying eggs, only to mature later into a rooster that not only crowed satisfactorily but sired two chicks as well. Most so-called hermaphrodites in rats, human beings, or swine, however, differ in secondary sexual characters but are not functionally bisexual at all.

The differentiation of sex organs is universal among higher plants. In the mosses and liverworts, sex cells are produced in archegonia (female) and antheridia (male) on a prominent haploid plant, the gametophyte. Most often these organs are produced on the same plant, which is therefore bisexual (homothallic), although unisexual (heterothallic) species are not uncommon. In the ferns and their allies sex organs are well defined and homothallism prevails. In these and higher plants, however, the diploid sporophyte is the prominent plant phase, with its distinguishing vascular and spore-producing systems. The gametophytes of seed-producing plants (flowering plants, conifers,

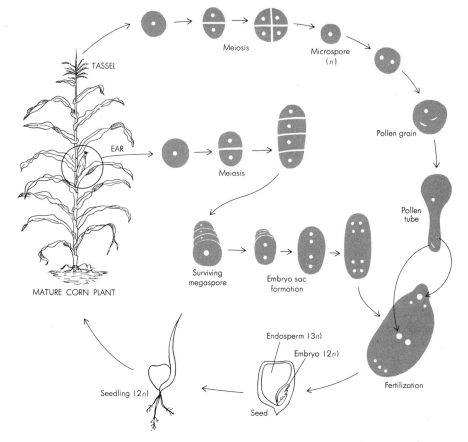

Fig. 2.1. The life cycle of corn. Fertilization involves both the union of one sperm (crescent shaped) with the egg to form the diploid or 2*n* embryo and the union of a second sperm with two nuclei in the embryo sac to form the triploid or 3*n* endosperm.

cycads) are greatly reduced and borne in distinct male and female organs, the stamen and pistil (Fig. 2.1). Fewer than 5 per cent of flowering plants are dioecious, with stamens and pistils confined to flowers in distinct male or female plants.

Sex chromosomes

A cytologically distinct pair of sex chromosomes provides the basis for sex determination in most higher animals and a few plants. The three most common types of sex-chromosome systems are the following:

$$XY \text{ type: } XX \; ♀ \quad XY \; ♂$$
$$XO \text{ type: } XX \; ♀ \quad X \; ♂$$
$$WZ \text{ type: } WZ \; ♀ \quad ZZ \; ♂$$

The XY type of sex inheritance predominates among vertebrate animals and is found among insects like *Drosophila* and dioecious plants like hops and hemp. In each case, females are homogametic (XX), i.e., they carry two X chromosomes; males are heterogametic (XY), i.e., their sperm segregates for the sex chromosome pair. The male determines the sex of his offspring by contributing X chromosomes to half the zygotes and Y chromosomes to the other half. Sex in the XY system is determined largely by the X chromosome. Development of female sex organs is triggered by threshold genes for femaleness located on the X chromosome. These genes must be present in double dose for the expression of femaleness. An extension of this postulate is that XY males with subthreshold femaleness genes are simply suppressed females. To a certain extent this is true in many animals.

The effect of polyploidy (increase in chromosome number) on the expression of sex in *Drosophila* led C. B. Bridges to formulate the balance theory of sex. Bridges observed that tetraploid flies with four sets of autosomes (chromosomes other than sex chromosomes) and four X chromosomes were female. In contrast, tetraploids with only two X chromomes were male (see Fig. **2.2**). Tetraploids having three X chromosomes, on the other hand, were neither one sex nor the other, and were described as intersexes. The effect of the X chromosome on femaleness seemed to be in balance with the action of the autosomes in promoting maleness. This balance is expressed in Fig. **2.2** by a ratio of X chromosomes to sets of autosomes, X/A. Extreme ratios of 0.3 and 1.5 were represented by the so-called supersexes, which, entirely sterile and weakly developed, do not seem particularly well described as "super." Bridge's data also show that maleness in *Drosophila* is not determined by the Y chromosome but by the autosomes. The Y chromosome—although virtually absent in monkeys and genetically inert in many insects, and often heterochromatic (cytologically irregular)—does have, however, a genetic role in the determination of maleness in many, if not most, vertebrate animals.

The total absence of one sex chromosome in the male characterizes the XO type of sex system. This type of sex determination occurs in

Number of sets (A) of autosomes	Sex chromosomes	$\frac{X}{A}$ ratio	Sex
2	XXX	1.5	Superfemale
2	XX or XXY	1.0	Female
4	XXXX	1.0	Female
4	XXX	0.75	Intersex
3	XX or XXY	0.67	Intersex
2	X or XY or XYY	0.5	Male
4	XX	0.5	Male
3	XY	0.3	Supermale

Fig. **2.2.** Sex expression in *Drosophila melanogaster*, as influenced by the changing ratios of sex chromosomes and autosomes.

an assortment of aphids, grasshoppers, and squash bugs, and is most important as a historic setting for our understanding of the action of sex chromosomes. Studying grasshopper cytology in 1902, C. E. Mc-Clung observed that males had only 21 chromosomes and he suggested that the unpaired chromosome was associated with sex. Later investigations of the squash bug *Anasa tristis* by E. B. Wilson revealed that females had 22 chromosomes and males but 21. Sexual differences were attributable to this odd or X-chromosome pair. Females carried both members of the unique pair, 20 + XX, while males carried only one, 20 + X. Insects like squash bugs appear to represent the endpoint in the progressive (or retrogressive) evolution of the Y chromosome, to its complete loss from the genome.

Intersexual XX/XY mosaics or gynandromorphs (*gyn* = female, *andro* = male) have been observed in many animals including man. Gynandromorphs often show intersexual development of secondary sexual characters. This is because of the action of sexual hormones, chemical regulants produced in one location of the body that act elsewhere to influence the development of organs and tissues. In animals lacking hormonal systems, gynandromorphs appear as striking mosaics of the primary sexual characters (sex-cell-producing organs). Brine shrimp gynandromorphs, for example, often produce eggs on one side of the body and sperm on the other. An example of hormonal effects on sex expression more familiar to the agriculturist is the freemartin calf. A freemartin is a sterile female calf; it is always born as the twin sister of a bull calf. Hormones produced by twin calf embryos may be transferred from one calf to the other whenever vascular connections chance to occur between the two fetuses. Male hormones appear earlier in development than do female hormones. When male and female twins are joined by vascular connections, the transfer of male hormones therefore suppresses normal development of the female calf, making her a sterile freemartin. In other animals, such as sheep, twins are never joined by vascular connections and freemartins are not found.

The female sex is heterogametic (WZ type) in birds, fish, and a variety of insects. The males have two identical sex chromosomes (the Z chromosomes), and the egg's genotype determines the sex of the offspring. This system was first described in poultry, but the inherent difficulties in studying poultry chromosomes leave an air of mystery about these birds. Although cocks are definitely ZZ (see Fig. 2.3), it is not clear whether the hen is ZW or ZO. Cytologists first reported chickens to have around 78 chromosomes, of which the majority were small microchromosomes. Genetic studies, however, revealed only 6 linkage groups, including the one linked with sex. Cytologists now interpret dividing cells in poultry to have 12 large chromosomes in

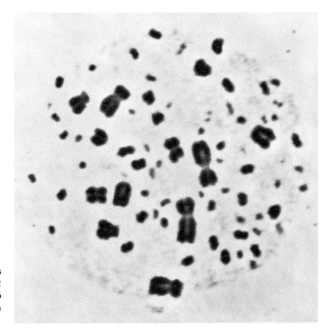

Fig. 2.3. Somatic chromosomes in a male fowl. There are 12 macrochromosomes and about 66 microchromosomes. Photograph courtesy of Earl H. Newcomer.

males and only 11 in females. Whether one of the microchromosomes in females is a greatly diminished W chromosome remains to be determined.

Sex linkage was also first discovered in poultry. William Bateson and R. C. Punnett found that feather barring is based on the action of a gene located on the Z chromosome. The partially dominant allele B produces a popular breed pattern ("barred") of white bars on dark feathers. In certain genetic backgrounds, two doses of B (occurring only in males) were shown by Punnett to reduce pigmentation to such an extent that the male birds were blotchy and pale in color. In stocks homozygous for B, therefore, the females $(B-)$ were always darker in plumage than were the males (BB). This difference, obvious even in baby chicks, permitted separation of the sexes (autosexing) without the usual labor and inherent errors of examining cloaca.

In a series of cleverly devised studies, silkworm geneticists in Japan similarly contrived sex-linked markers for autosexing. The male silkworm is quite superior to the female as a silk spinner. It is economically desirable, therefore, to eliminate the females in egg or early larval stages. Unfortunately, the males and females are almost indistinguishable at these stages. Genetic studies revealed that the female silkworms were heterogametic for sex chromosomes (ZW), while the males were homogametic (ZZ). By use of chromosomal translocations, the dominant black egg gene B was transferred from an autosome to the W chromosome. When females carrying the translocated W chromosome $(B-)$ were crossed with nonblack (bb) males, the hybrids were either female and black or male and colorless (see Fig. 2.4). The undesirable females then could be eliminated easily in either larval or egg stages by sexing machines.

Silkworms with two sets of autosomes and ZZW or ZZZW sex chromosomes are normal females. Apparently a female-determining locus on the W chromosome is fully dominant over male tendencies contributed by genes on other chromosomes. Although intersexes do not occur in silkworms, they are common in a related insect with the ZW–ZZ system, the destructive gypsy moth. Richard Goldschmidt made exhaustive studies of sex in the gypsy moth, using polyploid animals having different ratios of Z and W chromosomes. He concluded that the W chromosomes carried female determiners, as in silkworms. Varying degrees of intersexuality were viewed by Goldschmidt as the result of a quantitative relationship between female determiners and male determiners located both on the Z chromosome and on the autosomes. In an interesting and disastrous case of genetic curiosity, a silkworm grower introduced the gypsy moth into the United States in 1869, hoping that it would hybridize with the silkworm and contribute its cold-hardiness to the frost-susceptible silkworm. The cross failed, the gypsy moths escaped, and to this day they cause millions of dollars of damage annually to forest and fruit trees in the United States!

The unpaired sex chromosome Y or W, therefore, varies greatly in its genetic content in different organisms. In most species, some pairing occurs at meiosis between the X and Y or between the Z and W chromosomes. The sex-chromosome pair often divides precociously, ahead of the autosomes, suggesting that this homologous region is quite short.

Fig. 2.4. Distinction of male and female silkworm eggs and larvae by use of sex-linked marker, black. The black eggs (a) and larvae (b) are females. Photographs courtesy of Tadao Yokoyama.

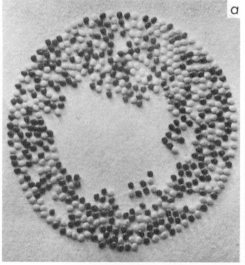
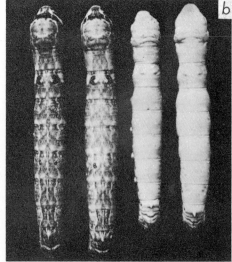

Fig. 2.5. Sex chromosomes of *Melandrium album* with suggested locations for. the female-suppressing (Su^F) and male-stimulating (M_1) genes in the Y chromosome. Shaded regions are homologous. Based on Mögens Westergaard, "Studies on Cytology and Sex Determination in Polyploid Forms of *Melandrium album*," *Dansk. Bot. Arkiv.*, 10 (1940), 1-131.

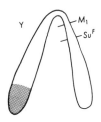

The two sex chromosomes rarely differ cytologically in higher plants, and their evolution is believed to be comparatively recent. In the garden pink *Melandrium*, for example, male plants are heterogametic (XY), and the Y chromosome is slightly larger than the X (see Fig. 2.5). The homologous region of the X and Y chromosomes is very short. The original differentiation of X and Y chromosomes in *Melandrium* is believed by Mögens Westergaard to have involved linkage of two genes on the Y chromosome. One gene, Su^F, suppressed pistil (female) development while the other gene, M_1, stimulated anther (male) development. These genes were dominant, but interacted with genes on the autosomes and X chromosome to produce hermaphrodites among certain polyploids. In *Melandrium*, as in most animals, the YY type is never recovered; this suggests that among the genes on the Y chromosome there is a recessive lethal (perhaps simply a loss of a vital gene present on the X chromosome).

Sex genes

Cytologically distinct sex chromosomes do not occur in the majority of unisexual plants or animals. In some of these such as the strawberry and the turkey, the females are heterogametic; in others such as asparagus, spinach, and many vertebrate animals, the males are heterogametic. A number of Mendelian factors suppress pistil or anther development in plants in a manner similar to the Su^F gene of *Melandrium*. These factors may properly be thought of as sex genes. The genetic synthesis of separate sexes was first demonstrated by R. A. Emerson and Donald F. Jones in corn, and has also been achieved in melons. Male and female flowers in corn are normally located in the tassel and ear respectively (see Fig. 2.1). Corn plants homozygous for any of several tassel-seed (*ts*) genes, however, produce female flowers and seeds in the tassel. Early Indian tribes cooked these seedy tassels to make popcorn bouquets, both attractive and edible. Several other genes in corn suppress development of female organs. Plants homozygous for the barrenstalk (*ba*) gene produce no ears at all. Plants of the genotype *babats₃ts₃*, for example, have no ears (*baba*) but produce seeds in their tassels (*ts₃ts₃*) and are, therefore, functionally female. Emerson produced plants having the genotype $babaTs_3ts_3$; these acted as males, having normal tassels but no ears. Crosses of these males with the $babats_3ts_3$ females produced the following pattern:

$$babats_3ts_3 \ (♀) \quad × \quad babaTs_3ts_3 \ (♂)$$
$$\downarrow$$
$$\tfrac{1}{2}\, babats_3ts_3 \ (♀\,♀) + \tfrac{1}{2}\, babaTs_3ts_3 \ (♂\,♂)$$

Future generations maintained the 1:1 sex ratio of functional males and females.

The sex genes of plants like corn and the watermelon appear simply to suppress normal development of one or the other sexual organ. A not entirely unrelated type of genetic system, first elucidated by P. W. and Anna Whiting, operates in many wasps, bees, and ants. The Whitings found that males in the parasitic wasp *Habrobracon* were commonly parthenogenetic haploids that could produce functional sperm by virtually avoiding meiosis. Although most diploid wasps were females, rare diploid males were also found. By the use of suitable marker genes, the diploid males were shown to be biparental (thus ruling out diploid parthenogenesis, also known to occur in insects). A significant observation was made concerning these diploid males; they occurred only as a result of matings of closely related individuals. Many of the eggs from these close matings failed to mature; the Whitings called these "bad eggs." It was shown that the bad eggs and biparental diploid males were homozygous for alleles at a sex locus, termed the X locus. In contrast, females were always heterozygous for X alleles. Brother–sister matings of the type $X_aX_b × X_a$ segregated $\tfrac{1}{3}$ females, $\tfrac{2}{3}$ males, and some bad eggs. The bad eggs rarely hatched, producing sterile diploid X_aX_a males (see Fig. 2.6). Many different X alleles were distinguished in these studies. Heterozygosity for X alleles was always essential for the expression of femaleness, for reasons as yet unknown. A similar multiple allelic sex locus probably governs sex in

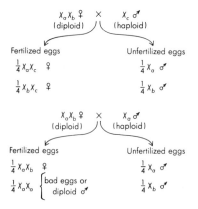

Fig. 2.6. Segregations of the sexes in *Habrobracon* wasps. The diagrammed matings involve a female, X_aX_b, with unrelated males, X_c, and with related males, X_a.

honeybees. Thus the queen bee who seeks her fortune abroad, rather than mating with one of her brothers or sons, probably does her matriarchy genetic honor.

Incompatibility

Algae, fungi, and lower animals

The multiple allelic sex loci of bees and wasps resemble, to a great extent, the incompatibility systems that promote outbreeding in protozoans, algae, fungi, and many higher plants. Each of these breeding systems involves alleles at a mating-type or incompatibility locus that cause the failure of certain matings. In many species of algae and fungi, mating occurs only when the haploid hyphae are genetically unlike. This kind of mating was termed heterothallic by A. F. Blakeslee, and the mating types were designated + and −. As a rule, the mating-type difference is conditioned by a single locus with two alleles. Compatibility between the + and − mating types results from a biochemical attraction between these genetically dissimilar hyphae.

Heterothallism is often associated with the infective ability of the rusts and smuts, parasitic fungi. The infective hyphae carry two haploid nuclei in each cell (termed dikaryons), one derived from each of the two parents, + and −. Monokaryons (+ or −) and the rare ++ and −− dikaryons are nonparasitic. Parasitism, therefore, depends on heterozygosity for the incompatibility locus. It remains to be determined why this relationship of infectivity and incompatibility exists. Incompatibility in bacteria is also determined by an apparently infective sex factor present in donor (F+) strains and absent in recipient (F−) strains. Thus matings of F+ and F+ or of F− and F− strains are incompatible as they are in other fungi. The unique viral-like infective properties of bacterial sex factors may be viewed as evolving from the simple +/− incompatibility system of other fungi.

Multiple alleles occur at the mating-type or incompatibility loci in most of the 16,000 different mushrooms and other heterothallic fungi. The haploid hyphae that grow from mushroom spores mate only when they carry different incompatibility alleles. As in the rusts and smuts, haploid nuclei do not fuse at the time the hyphae fuse, and a dikaryotic hypha results. The dikaryon grows into the mushroom's fruiting body above ground with which we are familiar. Nuclear fusion occurs late in the development of the fruiting body and it is followed immediately by meiosis and the ejection of the haploid spores. There are two types of multiple allelic incompatibility systems in mushrooms: the dipolar type, based on the action of alleles at a single locus, and the tetrapolar type, based on the action of alleles at two different loci. The number of naturally occurring alleles at each locus is very high, exceeding 100. The physiological basis for incompatibility in mushrooms has not been determined. It appears that unlike alleles attract and like alleles repel, somewhat like electric charges. There is no convenient biochemical explanation for this type of incompatibility reaction. Self-fertility also occurs in some fungi, such as the yeasts, and these species are said to be homothallic. In some instances, these have been shown to arise by mutation from heterothallic forms, perhaps upon the loss of the incompatibility locus.

Sexual reproduction in primitive, one-celled animals often involves mating types reminiscent of those in algae and fungi. The mating or conjugation occurs only among animals of different mating types. Basically the genetic control of mating resides in a single series of alleles. In *Euplotes patella*, six mating types arise from the three homozygous and three heterozygous combinations of three mating-type alleles (M). Each allele is responsible for a particular cellular protein, and heterozygotes contain two different proteins. The proteins stimulate mating between different mating types. Furthermore, they can be isolated in cell-free fluids and used to induce self-mating. For example, strain M_1M_1 cells will mate with other M_1M_1 cells when grown in fluid derived from M_2M_2 cells. In each of these instances, drawn from studies of lower organisms, mating-type or incompatibility loci promote genetic recombination by discouraging matings of closely related individuals.

Flowering plants

Three major types of incompatibility system—gametophytic, sporophytic, and heteromorphic—act to prevent self-fertilization among flowering plants. The gametophytic system is the most widespread of these, occurring among over half the plant families that have been studied intensively. Incompatibility is based on the action of alleles at a single locus, first demonstrated in flowering tobacco by E. M. East and A. J. Mangelsdorf. As in mushrooms, the numbers of alleles at loci in different plant species are very large, often exceeding forty. Incompatibility occurs as the result of the arrested growth of pollen tubes in the pistil. Thus it involves an interaction of haploid pollen tube and the diploid cells of the pistil. When a pollen grain contains an incompatibility allele that is present also in the style, tube growth is arrested. Only when the allele in the pollen is not present in the style can fertilization occur.

A plant of the genotype S_1S_2 produces pollen grains of two types, S_1 and S_2, in equal numbers. Both of these types are inhibited when placed on a pistil of the genotype S_1S_2, as in self-pollination (see Fig. 2.7). When pollen grains from a plant of the genotype S_1S_3 are placed on the S_1S_2 pistil, the S_1 pollen grains are inhibited, but the S_3 grains

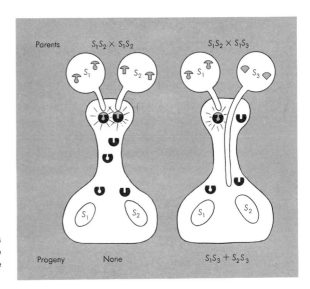

Fig. 2.7. Reactions of pollen and pistils during incompatible and compatible matings. Blips represent the antigen-like products of S allele action.

are not. Fertilization following this cross produces zygotes of the paternal genotype, S_1S_3, as well as of a new genotype, S_2S_3. The plants in each of these two genotypes are self-incompatible and cross-incompatible with each other. No dominance occurs among S alleles in the style. Incompatibility alleles act to inhibit self-fertilization, preventing in a similar manner cross-fertilization between vegetatively propagated plants of the same genotype. This fact was made only too clear to orchardists in the early 1900's. Large plantings of selected fruit trees became popular until it was recognized that incompatibility made these plantings almost completely fruitless! Pollinator plants are now added in orchards of almonds, plums, apples, passion fruits, and cherries, for example, to ensure that adequate pollen of compatible genotypes is available to permit normal fruit production. It is probable that the most primitive flowering plants were self-incompatible and that the outbreeding enforced by incompatibility encouraged the rapid evolution of flowering plants to a position of dominance in the world's flora. About half the genera of cultivated plants include self-incompatible species.

Self-fertility arises by mutation with relative ease in many species. Self-fertile mutants are induced readily by irradiation and represent, in large part, losses or deletions of the S locus. Pollen containing these mutants, referred to as S_f (self-fertility) alleles, are not inhibited in any styles. Polyploidy can also lead to self-fertility in otherwise self-incompatible species. Whereas the diploid plant produces pollen grains bearing a single S allele, tetraploids (having 4 sets of chromosomes) produce pollen having two S alleles. A tetraploid of the genotype $S_1S_1S_2S_2$ produces not only the homozygous S_1S_1 and S_2S_2 pollen, but also the heterozygous genotype S_1S_2. In many plants, pollen heterozygous for S alleles are uninhibited in styles of any genotype. Tetraploid plants carrying two alleles of this type are, therefore, both self-fertile and universally cross-fertile. The ability of mutations or polyploidy to change an outbreeding (self-incompatible) system to an inbreeding (self-fertile) system has important consequences in both the evolution and breeding of plant species.

A second type of incompatibility system, the sporophytic system, occurs in perhaps a third of the self-incompatible plants. It is distinguished from the gametophytic system by the fact that pollen phenotypes are determined by the maternal genotype. Thus a sporophytic-type heterozygote of the genotype S_1S_2 sheds pollen grains that are identical phenotypically with respect to incompatibility reaction, although they segregate genotypically. Since dominance commonly occurs among S alleles in the sporophytic system, pollen from S_1S_2 plants reacts like pollen from either the homozygous S_1S_1 or S_2S_2 plants. Pollen grains are of two cytological types in flowering plants, binucleate and trinucleate. Gametophytic incompatibility occurs primarily in plants with binucleate pollen, and sporophytic incompatibility occurs in plants with trinucleate pollen.

The sporophytic incompatibility systems of cabbages, broccoli, and other plants have been used in the production of hybrid seeds. Inbred lines homozygous for different incompatibility alleles are first produced. The inbreds, although highly self-incompatible, may be perpetuated successfully by self-pollinating immature flowers. The S-gene action in the pistil occurs rather late in the development of cabbage, tobacco, and other species and accounts for this self-fertility of young flower buds. When mature plants of one homozygous inbred, for example, S_1S_1, are planted together with plants of S_2S_2 or other inbreds, all of the seeds produced will be the result of hybridization between the inbred lines.

In the heteromorphic incompatibility system, first detailed by Darwin, incompatibility is correlated with certain differences in floral morphology. In the typical case, plants are of two types: the "pin" type, which has long pistils and short stamens, and the "thrum" type, which has short pistils and long stamens. Seeds are produced only when the two different types are crossed. Pollen germination or tube growth is inhibited in the crosses between pin and pin or between thrum and thrum. Genetic control of this inhibition is by a single incompatibility locus, S/s. Thrum plants carry the dominant S alleles and are commonly heterozygotes. Pin plants are always homozygous ss. The incompatibility alleles are linked closely with loci affecting pistil length (G/g) and stamen length (A/a) to give the following standard genotypes:

$$\text{Pin} \quad \frac{g \, s \, a}{g \, s \, a} \qquad \text{Thrum} \quad \frac{G \, S \, A}{g \, s \, a}$$

Rare crossovers result in the breakdown of this linked complex or supergene.

The multiple allelic S systems bear resemblance to multiple allelic blood-antigen systems in animals. The analogy has been drawn more closely by studies of the antiserums produced when proteins are extracted from pollen or styles of differing S-allele genotypes and injected into a rabbit. Antiserums obtained have specific affinity for proteins from the different allelic genotypes. Each S allele evidently governs the synthesis of a different protein. The manner in which stylar and pollen products of the same allele can interact to inhibit pollen growth is not known.

Graft incompatibilities in animals bear some resemblance to the incompatibilities of plants. Warm blooded animals commonly reject grafted tissues from other animals (except from an identical twin). At least fourteen different gene loci have been found to account for these histocompatibilities in rats and mice. Several of these loci are multiple allelic, and have been shown to act physiologically through the formation of antigens and antibodies.

Inbreeding and outbreeding

The genetic systems so far discussed—sex chromosomes, sex genes, incompatibility loci—exercise control over gene segregation and recombination. Each system affects the amount of mating between closely related individuals, or inbreeding, in a population. All degrees of inbreeding and its antithesis, outbreeding, may be found in animals and plants. At one extreme is a drastic form of inbreeding, self-fertilization, which occurs among perhaps a third of all crop plants and among many invertebrate animals. At the outbreeding extreme, higher animals and many plants cannot be self-fertilized and they commonly have biological barriers to matings between closely related individuals. These barriers may be genetic, as the cross sterility among sister plants often imposed by incompatibility alleles, or they may relate to dispersal mechanisms or migratory life as of birds and fish.

Man's attitude toward inbreeding has varied throughout the ages. In man, many primitive societies established rigid taboos against close marriages, perhaps sensing the deleterious effects of prolonged inbreeding. Nonetheless, some of the most vigorous early civilizations—Greek, Egyptian, Hebrew, Nordic—practiced incest conscientiously. The Pharaohs married their own sisters so as not to dilute the bloodlines of their gods, and pedigrees of Greek heroes have been likened to those of our highly inbred race horses. The shift away from inbreeding in man took place perhaps more for social than for biological reasons, since the effects of inbreeding become pronounced only if prolonged over many generations.

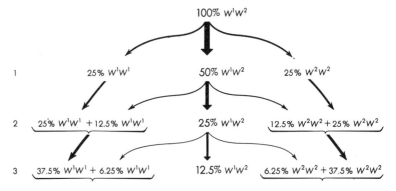

Fig. 2.8. The reduction of heterozygosity in a population segregating for the W alleles following self-fertilization.

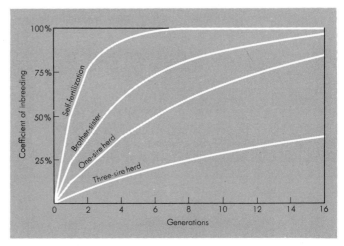

Fig. 2.9. Coefficients of inbreeding under different systems of mating involving recurrent inbreeding. Based on calculations of Sewall Wright.

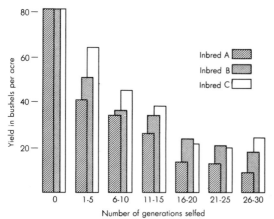

Fig. 2.10. The influence of thirty generations of self-fertilization on yield in corn. Data are given for three different inbred lines. Based on experiments of Donald F. Jones.

Outbreeding systems tend to promote genetic variability while inbreeding promotes genetic constancy. The genetic constancy of inbred lines clearly results from homozygosity. We can view this in its simplest form by considering the segregation of alleles at a single locus during continued self-fertilization (Fig. 2.8). The self-pollination of a heterozygote produces the familiar 1:2:1 genotypic ratio. In effect, the proportion of heterozygous individuals is reduced in this one generation by a half. Each succeeding generation of self-fertilization also reduces the proportion of heterozygotes by a half; in the nth inbred generation, it equals $(\frac{1}{2})^n$. All remaining genotypes, or $1 - (\frac{1}{2})^n$, will be homozygous for the locus under study. The important role of $1 - (\frac{1}{2})^n$ is discussed in the following section on the coefficient of inbreeding under self-fertilization.

If we assume population to be infinitely large, an amount of heterozygosity equal to $(\frac{1}{2})^n$ will remain even after prolonged self-fertilization. That *if*, however, introduces one of the most important qualifications of inbreeding behavior, namely, that of population size. No biologist can work with (or afford) a population of infinite size. If a virus were to hit the third inbred generation (see Fig. 2.8), leaving only a single individual alive (an "inbreeding crisis"), chances are very good (6 out of 8) that this individual would be homozygous. When all the members of a population are homozygous for a certain allele, we say that fixation has occurred for that allele. Rates of fixation increase as population sizes decrease.

Sister-brother or sib mating, the most intense inbreeding possible in higher animals, produces a much less rapid approach to homozygosity than self-fertilization produces. Figure 2.9 shows the approach to homozygosity for self-fertilized and sib-fertilized populations and for herds in which unrelated sires were used for all matings. Even with sib mating, the homozygosity for a single locus exceeds 90 per cent after ten generations of inbreeding (which takes a long half-century for cattle or sheep and would take almost three centuries for man). Rates of approach to homozygosity for traits based on two or more segregating loci are much less than for monogenic traits. The search for domesticated animals homozygous for traits based on many genes is, therefore, a predictably fruitless task.

The appearance of deleterious recessive traits is the most striking single effect of inbreeding. Deleterious recessive alleles are frequent in all outbreeding species. Inbreeding increases greatly the probability that any particular subvital recessive allele will become homozygous. A few generations of self-fertilization in corn, clover, or cabbage, for example, demonstrate vividly the effects of subvital recessive genes (see Fig. 2.10). Reduction in seed set, in fertility of pollen, in growth rate, and in plant size and vigor occur with virtually any starting materials when inbreeding is practiced in these and similar crops. Many advanced inbreds fail to reproduce at all.

Inbreeding depression may be viewed primarily as the result of homozygosity for subvital alleles. The depressing effect of inbreeding on yield may be prolonged over many generations. This is illustrated in Fig. 2.10 for three corn inbreds studied by Donald F. Jones. Virtual homozygosity for the many genes influencing yields occurred after about twenty generations of self-fertilization. In contrast, the same lines were found to be homozygous for genes influencing height after only five generations of self-fertilization.

Equally dramatic as the effects of inbreeding in plants is the appearance of recessive dwarfism, hairlessness, and other subvital genotypes following close matings of animals like cattle. Here the value of each calf is great enough to make each deleterious homozygote an economic loss. A passionate devotion to breed purity has led animal lovers to create a high degree of inbreeding in many domesticated animals, but nowhere is this so striking as in fur-bearing animals. Since growers of these animals often have only small populations, they feel obliged to breed even the worst of them and many lines have simply "run out," largely because of inbreeding depression. It should be noted, however, that continued self-fertilization does not necessarily destroy a species. Inbreeding quickly purges a species of deleterious genes, and the surviving genotypes may be more or less unaffected by further inbreeding after ten or twenty generations.

While natural inbreeding is rare in animals, it is relatively common among plants. Almost half of the economically important plants are self-pollinated, although many have varying degrees of natural cross-pollination. Some examples of self-pollinated and cross-pollinated crops follow.

> Largely self-pollinated: wheat, rice, barley, peanuts, soybeans, tobacco, tomatoes, peppers, peas, beans, apricots, citrus fruits, peaches, cotton, sorghum.
> Largely cross-pollinated: corn, rye, sugar beets, cucumbers, carrots, celery, cabbage and its relatives, apples, grapes, plums, almonds, raspberries, strawberries, orchids.

The degree of natural inbreeding in higher plants is influenced by a rich assortment of characters. In most plants, a balance has evolved between self- and cross-fertilization: as one promotes genetic constancy the other promotes vigor (heterosis or hybrid vigor) and genetic variability. Genetic constancy is characteristic not only of inbreds but also of hybrids obtained by crossing two inbreds. Artificial hybrids of long-term inbreds thus have the combined advantages of genetic constancy and of hybrid vigor (see Chapter 5).

Coefficient of inbreeding

Two measures applied by the geneticist to populations in which inbreeding has occurred, i.e., in which some individuals are related by descent, are the degree of genetic relationship and the coefficient of inbreeding. In the absence of inbreeding, any two individuals will have no common ancestor; their degree of genetic relationship will be zero. Fifty per cent of an individual's genes come from each parent, 25 per cent from each grandparent, 12.5 per cent from each great-grandparent, and so on. Brothers have an average of 50 per cent of their genes in common, or a genetic relationship of 50 per cent. Consider the following pedigree, in which a fine bull, B, is mated to one of his daughters, C, to produce a calf, D.

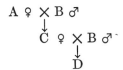

How do we determine the degree of genetic relationship between D and his parent-grandparent B? In the first place, 50 per cent of D's genes were obtained directly from his father. However, D also obtained B's genes indirectly through his mother. Since $\frac{1}{2}$ of C's genes were from B, and $\frac{1}{2}$ of D's genes were from C, we may calculate that $\frac{1}{2} \times \frac{1}{2}$ or $\frac{1}{4}$ of D's genes are B's genes that came to D by way of C. Therefore, D is related to B by $\frac{1}{2} + \frac{1}{4} = \frac{3}{4}$ (degree of genetic relationship $= 75$ per cent).

Degrees of relationship may be used in a general way to express the relationship of a breed to a favorite bull, such as the famous Shorthorn bull Favourite. Although he died in the early 1800's, Favourite had a genetic relationship in 1920 of almost 55 per cent to the entire Shorthorn breed in England! Genetic relationships prove useful to breeders in judging the merits of untested animals who are related to animals of known merit. The use of degree of relationship is clear to the average farmer, who will offer you a much better price for the full sister of your prize-winning cow or race horse than for one of its cousins, nieces, or more distant relatives.

The coefficient of inbreeding, symbolized by F, is a widely used measure of inbreeding. Sewall Wright formulated the coefficient to measure the increase of homozygosity in a population due to inbreeding. Inbreeding involves the mating of individuals that are related by descent as in the following pedigree.

The essential results of inbreeding are that two individuals related by descent (as D and E) may carry identical genes from the common ancestor B, and that these genes in turn may become homozygous in offspring F. The coefficient of inbreeding measures the homozygosity contributed in this way by inbreeding.

In the general case, the coefficient of inbreeding gives the probability that the 2 genes at any locus in an individual are identical by descent, i.e., that they are both derived by replication from a gene in the common ancestor. Applied to the population, it estimates the increased homozygosity contributed by inbreeding. For the pedigree illustrated above, the coefficient of inbreeding gives the probability that animal F is homozygous at any locus for alleles present in common ancestor B. The coefficient of inbreeding is equal to $(\frac{1}{2})^n$, where n is the number of individuals in the pedigree path leading from the inbred animal to his common ancestor and back again. The path here leads from F to E, then to B, and back again through D; n, therefore, is equal to 3. The probability that animal F is homozygous for a particular gene present in B is, therefore, $(\frac{1}{2})^3$ or 12.5 per cent. In terms of all genes, F is homozygous for 12.5 per cent of the alleles present in B. In the event that the common ancestor is inbred, adjustment must be made for its coefficient of inbreeding (symbolized as F_A). The coefficient of inbreeding in such an inbreeding pedigree becomes $(\frac{1}{2})^n$ plus $(\frac{1}{2})^n (F_A)$, commonly expressed as

$$F = (\tfrac{1}{2})^n (1 + F_A)$$

For more complicated cases in which there are several common ancestors, F becomes the sum of the F values for each ancestor in the pedigree. Inbreeding coefficients in large animal populations rarely exceed 0.1 (10 per cent), although they have been known to increase to figures above 25 per cent in closely bred herds. An inbred line of poultry is defined legally in the United States as one that has an average coefficient of inbreeding of 37.5 per cent or more, the equivalent of two generations of brother-sister mating. At higher levels of F, the likelihood of homozygosity for deleterious alleles and inbreeding depression is so great that further inbreeding may be economically unwise, unless the inbreds are to be recombined into hybrids (as in poultry).

For systems in which self-fertilization can be practiced, the coefficient of inbreeding may be calculated by

$$F \text{ (self-fertilization)} = 1 - (\tfrac{1}{2})^n + (\tfrac{1}{2})^n F_A$$

In this equation, n is the number of generations of selfing and F_A is again the inbreeding coefficient of the common ancestor—a plant, for example, in which the self-fertilization was started. If A, with which selfing begins, is not inbred at all, F_A equals zero and the equation reduces to $F = 1 - (\frac{1}{2})^n$. We have noted in a previous section that this equation expresses the percentage of homozygotes in a self-fertilizing population derived from a hybrid.

Detailed consideration of inbreeding coefficients can be found in treatises on genetics and selection by Oscar Kempthorne, I. M. Lerner, C. C. Li, and J. L. Lush.

References

Li, C. C. *Population Genetics*. Chicago: University of Chicago Press, 1955. See especially Chapters 12 and 13 on genetic relationships and inbreeding.

McKusick, Victor A., *Human Genetics*. Englewood Cliffs, N.J.: Prentice-Hall, Inc., 1964. For details of sex genetics in the best-known mammal.

Peters, J. A., ed., *Classic Papers in Genetics*. Englewood Cliffs, N.J.: Prentice-Hall, Inc., 1961. The papers by T. H. Morgan, A. H. Sturtevant, and C. B. Bridges (1925) should become familiar to all students.

Problems

2.1. Diploid males of *Habrobracon* very rarely produce viable sperm. If a male of this type mated with his sister, what segregation would occur for sex types?

2.2. Immature styles in a petunia of the genotype S_3S_4 (gametophytic-type incompatibility) were self-pollinated. The progenies were allowed to intercross at random, producing abundant seed. Plants grown from these intercross seeds were isolated for seed increase, but they failed to produce seeds. Why?

2.3. If 40 per cent of the plants in a wheat field are heterozygous at a given locus, what proportion would be homozygous at this locus after two generations of self-fertilization?

2.4. The pedigree below is presented in arrow style; thus, F is the offspring of D and P, D is the offspring of C and B, and so forth. Calculate the inbreeding coefficient for F when the inbreeding coefficient of B is 20 per cent.

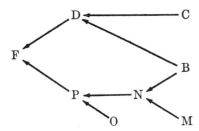

2.5. What is the coefficient of inbreeding of a child whose parents are first cousins?

Discontinuous Variation

The phenotypic variation in a segregating population may be of two types—continuous or discontinuous. The corresponding genes may be described as primarily quantitative or qualitative in their effects. Genes influencing weight, productivity, and height exemplify the first class, while genes that govern blood groups and coat-color patterns of animals illustrate the second class. This is an intentionally oversimplified classification that serves merely as a guide to examination of genetic traits, but it is in no sense a law that genes inevitably obey.

Since the time of Mendel, genetic traits that segregate in a discontinuous manner have perhaps been accorded more than their fair share of genetic attention. The pragmatic agricultural extension specialist often questions the dollars-and-cents value of studying vinegar flies with forked bristles or chickens with black skins. Economically important traits like beefsteak tenderness and egg production do not segregate simply and may seem unrelated genetically to these monogenic traits. Our knowledge of quantitative genetics, however, builds on an understanding of the actions and interactions of single genetic factors. Monogenic traits also serve as useful genetic markers in animal and plant improvement, and certain of them (e.g., genetic lethals) are most important in agriculture.

Allelic action and interaction

We recognize a gene only when it exists in two or more forms or alleles. Alleles occupy the same locus on homologous chromosomes and, by definition, are mutually exclusive; when one occupies the locus on a particular chromosome, another cannot. Any new allele may be characterized at once in two different ways—by its phenotypic effect when it is homozygous and by its phenotypic effect when it is combined in heterozygotes with its sister alleles. In short, alleles are known by their actions and interactions.

Three major classes of alleles can be distinguished—amorphs, hypomorphs, and neomorphs. The linamarase locus (Li/li) in white clover illustrates the common amorphic type of gene action. Li is responsible for the formation of a single enzyme, linamarase, that breaks down a glucoside in clovers to form the poisonous hydrogen cyanide. Clover strains carrying the Li alleles are, therefore, undesirable as forage plants. The dominance of Li over its allele li is seen in the phenotypic identity of the genotypes $Lili$ and $LiLi$; linamarase is formed in similar amounts in the two genotypes. In $lili$ homozygotes linamarase is absent and cyanide is not formed. Alleles like li are amorphs or inactive alleles which act as genetic blocks to normal biosynthesis. In its broadest sense, an amorph may be an allele that is inoperative, one that fails to produce a measurable effect, or even the absence or deletion of a gene (it is often impossible to distinguish among these conditions).

Hypomorphs are alleles that function imperfectly in comparison with wild-type alleles. Sometimes known as leaky genes, they are prevalent among induced mutations. The mutation from amorphic alleles back to their wild-type precursors has been studied extensively in the mold *Neurospora*. Mutants that lack the ability to produce adenine, for example, have been tested for backmutations to allelic forms that permit synthesis of this vital purine. Quantitative studies of the activity of these backmutations reveal that the vast majority of them are hypomorphs that permit adenine synthesis, but at levels much below that of the wild-type allele.

The hair or fur of most rodents and mammals contains a dark pigment, melanin. Variations in melanin content occur under the control of alleles at the C locus. Sewall Wright studied the interactions in guinea pigs of alleles C (agouti), c^r (extreme dilution), c^d (dark chinchilla) and c^a (albino). Guinea pigs heterozygous or homozygous for the C allele were equally dark. Assigning the value of 100 per cent to melanin contents in these animals, Wright obtained the following values for the melanin in other C allelic combinations (in animals of the genotype $BB\ EE\ PP$): $c^r c^r = 81\%$, $c^r c^a = 42\%$, $c^a c^a = 0\%$
$$c^d c^d = 67\%, \quad c^d c^a = 39\%, \quad c^a c^a = 0\%$$
$$c^r c^r = 81\%, \quad c^r c^d = 72\%, \quad c^d c^d = 67\%$$

The alleles c^r and c^d are shown by these data to be hypomorphs and the allele c^a an amorph. In heterozygotes dominance is lacking among them, i.e., their effects are additive. As we have noted above, however, each is recessive to the wild-type agouti allele.

Neomorphic alleles are best illustrated by those governing blood serum antigens in animals. As many as 150 different alleles have been found at a single locus in cattle. Each allele appears to act as a template for a protein with antigenic properties. Relatively minor changes (neomorphs) of the DNA structure of the gene are believed to produce amino-acid sequence changes in proteins, changing their antigenic specificity. Neomorphs differ qualitatively in their action, and are not related in quantitative series, as we observed in regard to hypomorphs. Heterozygotes of neomorphs commonly display the allelic products of both alleles. Alleles that govern the leaf marking patterns of many plants act as neomorphs, each producing a different type of marking. Heterozygotes commonly produce two different markings. Allelic interactions of three of the ten leaf marking alleles of white clover are illustrated in Fig. 3.1. Pattern superimpositions similar to those in clover also occur for alleles that govern markings in insects and serum proteins in animals. It is probable that most multiple alleles are neomorphs with independent action in heterozygotes.

Dominance is the major form of interaction between alleles. It may or may not be an intrinsic property of alleles themselves. Several instances are known of the modification or even reversal of dominance by genes at other loci. In one intensively studied example of dominance modifiers, the dark protective coloration of certain moths was found to

Fig. 3.1. Allelic actions and interactions producing white leaf markings in white clover. Homozygotes and heterozygotes are shown for three alleles—V^b (broken V), V^f (filled V), and V^h (high V).

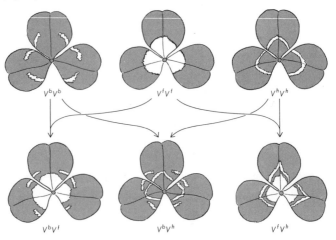

be governed by a single gene. Dominance of the dark form over color-less occurred in some moth populations. In other populations domi-nance was absent and the hybrids were intermediate to their parents. The same coloration genes were found in both populations, but modify-ing genes accentuating dominance of the dark form occurred only in the former one.

Two other types of alleles have been proposed by H. J. Muller—hypermorphs and antimorphs. Hypermorphs are alleles that produce an excess amount of a product, the antithesis of hypomorphs. *Excess* is defined here in terms of the wild-type alleles, which usually are con-sidered to represent a physiological optimum of gene action. The role of hypermorphic alleles in hybrid vigor will be considered in Chapter 5. Antimorphs are alleles with an action opposed to that of the wild type; they are uncommon and perhaps poorly defined.

Nonallelic gene interaction

Within months of the rediscovery of Mendel's paper exceptions were reported to the monogenic ratios obtained for independently as-sorting traits. The initial exceptions proved upon analysis to be digenic segregations involving two loci, illustrated brilliantly by William Bate-son in studies of the colors of sweet pea flowers and Wyandotte chick-ens. Evidence for multigenic segregations, involving three or more loci, soon followed. The simultaneous segregations of two loci, dominance assumed, result in the following ratios in F_2 populations.

$$AaBb \times \\ AaBb \rightarrow \begin{array}{l} 9\ A^- B^-\ (= 1\ AABB + 2\ AaBB + 2\ AABb + 4\ AaBb) \\ 3\ aaB^-\ (= 1\ aaBB + 2\ aaBb) \\ 3\ A^- bb\ (= 1\ AAbb + 2\ Aabb) \\ 1\ aabb \end{array}$$

Nonallelic interactions involving two loci result in variations on this scheme. Conventional modifications include the following ratios, to-gether with the groupings from 9:3:3:1 with which they can be equated.

$$
\begin{array}{ll}
9{:}7 & = 9{:}(3+3+1) \\
13{:}3 & = (9+3+1){:}3 \\
12{:}3{:}1 & = (9+3){:}3{:}1 \\
15{:}1 & = (9+3+3){:}1
\end{array}
$$

The interpretation of digenic ratios has led to the definition of three basic types of nonallelic gene interaction. Together with common asso-ciated digenic ratios, these are

Duplicate gene interaction	15:1
Complementary gene interaction	9:7
Modifier gene interaction	13:3, 12:3:1

Duplicate loci are commonplace among higher plants, largely resulting from the multiplication of chromosome sets (polyploidy). By definition, duplicate loci perform the same function. If dominance occurs at both loci, the F_2 digenic ratio of 15:1 is obtained, in which all genotypes except the recessive homozygote resemble the dominant homozygote. Duplicate loci may arise in the course of evolution because of irregularities in crossing over that result in neighboring ("tandem") repeats. The bar eye of *Drosophila* is a classic example. Loci may also occur in triplicate or higher multiples in polyploids such as wheat and timothy grass.

Complementary loci can be illustrated by the synthetic pathway of a given product P_n, which is catalyzed at successive steps by enzymes contributed by interacting loci.

$$\begin{array}{ccc} \text{gene } A_1 & & \text{gene } B_1 \\ \downarrow & & \downarrow \\ \text{enzyme } A_1 & & \text{enzyme } B_1 \\ \end{array}$$
$$P_0 \longrightarrow P_1 \longrightarrow \ldots \to P_n$$

Complementary gene action involving two loci, such as those illustrated, often arises when both enzymes (and corresponding active alleles A_1 and B_1) are requisite to completion of the biosynthesis. When dominance is present at each locus ($A_1 > A_0$ and $B_1 > B_0$), the characteristic 9:7 ratio of F_2 progeny is obtained. The $\frac{7}{16}$ includes all genotypes homozygous for recessive alleles A_0 and B_0. Other models can be devised for complementary gene action, of which the following is perhaps most common:

$$\begin{array}{l} \quad\quad \text{enzyme } A_1 \\ P_0 \longrightarrow P_1 \\[4pt] \quad\quad \text{enzyme } B_1 \\ P_2 \longrightarrow P_3 \end{array} \Bigg\} \longrightarrow \ldots \to P_n$$

Modifier genes suppress or modify the action of other loci, and may or may not have a phenotypic effect when alone. Many genes have been described in *Drosophila* and *Neurospora*, for example, that modify a mutant phenotype toward the normal, causing an apparent reversion of the mutant to wild type. These often mimic the hypomorphic backmutations described previously. Modifier genes of this type are spoken of as suppressors; that is, they suppress the mutant gene. Dilution and intensifier genes are among the common types of modifiers, many of which produce important variations in pigmentation. Inhibitors are dominant modified genes that prevent the expression of other loci. The several classes of modifying genes exist as an intergrading series, of which abundant examples may be cited in most organisms.[1]

Whenever dominance is complete and only two loci are involved, nonallelic interactions provide an intriguing mathematical mélange of discontinuous segregations. However, the absence of dominance, the increase in the number of loci, the presence of hypomorphic alleles, or the linkage of interacting loci can introduce important complications to analysis. Each can lead to the loss of clear-cut ratios in segregating lines. Together, they conspire to provide the basis for continuous genetic variation, a subject to which we shall turn in the following chapter.

Lethal factors

Recessive zygotic lethals

In 1902, an outstanding Holstein bull, Prinz Adolph, was introduced into Sweden from Germany. His descendants quickly proved their mettle and were valued highly for breeding purposes. So much were they prized, in fact, that by 1930 the genes of Prinz Adolph were distributed among more than 2,000 registered bulls in northern Europe. During these years, there occurred an alarming increase in the number of births of hairless calves. The hairless animals could not control body temperature and died within a few minutes of birth. Genetic studies revealed that hairless animals were homozygous for a recessive zygotic lethal factor. Heterozygotes or carriers of this factor could not be distinguished from normal animals.

Zygotic lethal factors like that of Prinz Adolph, also referred to as embryo lethals or somatic lethals, cause the death of an organism before sexual maturity. In practice, they are of greatest importance in higher animals and man, where each individual is valued highly. The estimated loss to cattle growers as a result of Prinz Adolph's hairless factor alone runs into millions of dollars. A fifth or more of the developing embryos of man, sheep, and other mammals abort *in utero;* many of these abortions, it is suspected, result from the action of embryo lethal factors.

Zygotic lethal factors are prevalent also in plants. In pine trees, blueberry bushes, walnut trees, alfalfa, and many other plants, self-pollination results in a twofold to fivefold increase in seed abortion,

---

[1] The term *epistatic* (epi - above, static - placed) was coined by Bateson in reference to genes that act as dominant modifiers of nonallelic genes. The term has since been broadened by some authors to include other types of gene interaction. I have avoided use of this term here, however, in favor of the more inclusive *nonallelic gene interaction.*

as compared with cross-pollination. For example, when pine trees are self-pollinated, almost 50 per cent of the seeds are embryoless. When the same trees are cross-pollinated, however, less than 10 per cent of the seeds are embryoless. It must be concluded that species such as these are heterozygous for a large number of recessive lethal factors. Inbreeding increases greatly the likelihood of homozygosity for such factors.

The early detection of recessive lethals in a prize bull like Prinz Adolph is of considerable economic importance. The geneticist may rule out the possibility that a bull carries a recessive lethal by mating him with 23 of his own heifer calves, with 19:1 odds against random error. In order to be very safe (99:1 odds), 35 testcross matings must be made. These estimates are based on the fact that half of the heifer calves would carry their father's recessive lethal factor, and matings of these carrier heifers with their father would segregate only 25 per cent homozygous recessives. The expected frequency of mutant lethal ·offspring from the father–daughter crosses, therefore, is $\frac{1}{2} \times \frac{1}{4}$, or $\frac{1}{8}$. The numbers 23 (19:1 odds) and 35 (99:1 odds) derive from the fact that $\frac{7}{8}$ raised to the twenty-third power is about 5 per cent, while $\frac{7}{8}$ raised to the thirty-fifth power is about 1 per cent. Father–daughter test matings of this type in beef cattle have segregated recessive lethals like amputated (13 out of 115 animals), moose calf (11 out of 55 animals), and hairless (12 out of 110 animals). Amputated occurred in a prize Swedish Holstein bull, Gallus, and was transmitted to almost 3,000 of his great-grandsons before its detection. In contrast, the prize bull Amor was found to be a carrier of the moose calf lethal before his talents were too widely exploited. Unfortunately, the effect of a recessive lethal is felt less in the immediate generation than in advanced generations. Untested yearling bull calves have been sold for prices as high as $200,000, even though they may carry recessive lethals that would cause millions of dollars of damage to the cattle industry.

Zygotic lethals like hairless and moose calf are called obligate lethals, since none of the homozygous animals survive under any environmental circumstances. A hairless trait similar to that of Prinz Adolph occurs as a recessive lethal in the Guernsey breed of dairy cattle. When pains are taken to keep hairless Guernseys warm, however, they may be grown to sexual maturity. Lethals of this type are called facultative lethals. Nakedness in chickens is a facultative lethal trait that might once have been a boon to chicken pluckers (Fig. 3.2). About half the eggs that are homozygous for the gene naked fail to hatch. Many of those that do hatch, however, will survive if raised to maturity in a heated chickenhouse, since they have poor control of body heat loss and are cold most of the time. Indirectly, this affects

Fig. 3.2. Naked, a facultative lethal trait in a three-week-old chicken. Photograph courtesy of F. B. Hutt; from *Genetics of the Fowl* (McGraw-Hill, 1949), reproduced by permission.

every major organ in the bare bird, leading to enlargement of its spleen, pancreas, heart, and gizzard, causing a wide variety of abnormalities. These associated phenotypic effects of a gene's action are known as pleiotropic effects.

Pleiotropism is illustrated in a most striking way by many lethal and sublethal factors, and often aids in the early diagnosis of the lethal condition. In the case of *diabetes mellitus* in animals, the primary genetic change is an obscure degeneration and malfunction of the islets of Langerhans, cellular structures in the pancreas. The loss of insulin normally produced by these cells affects endocrine function, which in turn affects the liver's metabolism of proteins and fats, leading to excretion of sugar in the urine. Among these pleiotropic effects of diabetes gene action, sugar excretion is the symptom conventionally used to diagnose the genetic condition.

Zygotic lethals lacking dominance

Many zygotic lethal factors lack dominance, that is, the heterozygote can be distinguished phenotypically from both homozygotes. Droopy-winged bees nicely illustrate this condition. Early studies indicated that droopy-winged bees were always females (workers) while the males (drones) were never droopy. Segregations among the worker females showed droopy to be a monogenic lethal trait, acting as follows.

$$D_1D_1 = \text{lethal}$$
$$D_0D_1 = \text{droopy}$$
$$D_0D_0 = \text{normal}$$

In contrast to the female bees, which are diploid, the males are haploid. With respect to the droopy locus, therefore, males can be of only two different genotypes.

$$D_1 = \text{lethal}$$
$$D_0 = \text{normal}$$

The mystery of the missing droopy drones is hereby solved. Since drones cannot be heterozygous, they cannot be droopy.

The nondominant lethal condition was first discovered in mice. Yellow-bodied mice always segregated wild-type (agouti) offspring. From matings of yellow mice with yellow mice, the unique segregation of 2,386 yellow : 1,235 agouti was obtained. The 2:1 ratio was interpreted by W. E. Castle to indicate that a third phenotype, acting as a lethal to the embryos *in utero*, was not recovered. Assuming that the lethals were produced as frequently as normals, the familiar 1:2:1 ratio of lethal to yellow to normal could be calculated. The nondominant lethal condition was soon verified in studies of a short-legged breed of cattle known as Dexter, popularized in the nineteenth century. Dexters did not breed true, however, their progeny often "reverting" to the long-legged type. Analysis of the matings between Dexters revealed that about one-fourth of the calves were bulldogs, born dead with extremely short legs and other bones (a condition known as chondrodystrophy, common among mammals).

$$\text{Dexter } (D_0D_1) \times \text{Dexter } (D_0D_1)$$
$$\downarrow$$
$$\tfrac{1}{4} \text{ Bulldog } (D_0D_0) + \tfrac{2}{4} \text{ Dexter } (D_0D_1) + \tfrac{1}{4} \text{ Normal } (D_1D_1)$$

It seems best to avoid the term *dominance* in the description of traits like bulldog calf. However, similar traits are often described, somewhat awkwardly, as "recessive lethals with dominant visible effects." In practice, lethals that have a phenotypic effect in the heterozygote are symbolized by capital letters, such as Cp (Creeper fowl), Pl (Platinum fox), or Ha (Mexican hairless dog), and are often referred to as dominant lethals. A fully dominant lethal factor, however, technically can be studied only at the moment it occurs or acts, that is, as a dominant lethal mutation.

Gametic lethals

Gametic lethals prevent the normal maturation or function of sex cells. They are commonly associated with aberrations of chromosomal structure or number. For example, the separation of chromosomes that have exchanged segments at meiosis leads to chromosomal losses or deletions from about 50 per cent of the gametes. Unless the losses are extremely minute, the deficient gametes fail to mature properly, and are often shed as sterile sex cells. Gametic semilethality cannot be observed among the mature pollen or sperm cells of many organisms, probably because the genetic deficiencies lead to early abortion of the sperm-forming cells. Gametic sterility is common in polyploids (see Chapter 6).

Gametic lethals used in the production of hybrid corn, onions, and other plants involve the interaction of male-sterile genes with cytoplasmic factors, referred to as cytoplasmic male steriles. The inheritance of cytoplasmic male sterility (or simply, cytosterility) is maternal, since the cytoplasm of a zygote is obtained only from the egg and not from the pollen (see Fig. 3.3). Thus onions with the S (sterile) cytoplasm and the genotype *ms ms* (male sterile) produce shriveled anthers with aborted pollen grains. Any combination involving the normal cytoplasm N produces normal pollen. Similarly, any combination having the male-fertile allele Ms produces normal pollen. Since the S *ms ms* lines are pollen sterile, they can be perpetuated only by crossing with a fertile counterpart, usually F *ms ms*. Hybrid seeds for

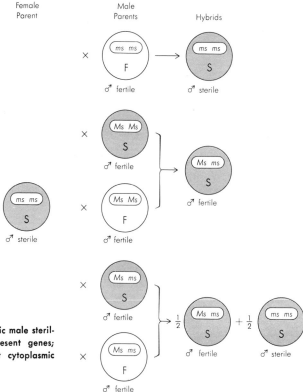

Fig. 3.3. Inheritance of cytoplasmic male sterility. Letters in inner circles represent genes; letters in outer circles represent cytoplasmic reactions.

Fig. 3.4. Use of cytoplasmic male sterility in the production of hybrid corn. Lines designated "Sheds no pollen" are cytosterile, while lines designated "Pollinator" carry restorer genes. Photograph courtesy of Funk Bros. Seed Co., Bloomington, Illinois.

the market are produced by interplanting the S ms ms counterpart of one parent with the F ms ms counterpart of the second parent. Seed is saved only from the S ms ms plants, and F_1 hybrids grown from these seeds are also male sterile.

In corn and sorghum breeding it is imperative that some of the hybrids produce pollen in the farmer's field. Genes that overcome the sterility imposed by the sterile cytoplasm, that is, genes that restore fertility, must therefore be incorporated into the pollen parent (Fig. 3.4). Cytosterile hybrids that have these restorer genes produce functional pollen and can serve as pollen parents for seed production in the fields of hybrid plants. Two dominant restorer genes, R_{f1} and R_{f2}, are used commercially to restore fertility to corn plants with the sterile cytoplasm. The commercial value of this system is indicated by the fact that it is the only genetic method to have a United States patent.

The S cytoplasm provides a rather interesting biological puzzle to plant geneticists. How can a cytoplasm be lethal to a pollen grain, and in what way do nuclear genes interact with this cytoplasmic factor? An intriguing possibility emerges from electron-microscopic observations of unique cytoplasmic inclusions in cytoplasmically sterile plants. It is suspected that these inclusions are virus particles that survive only in plants with a virus-susceptible genotype (ms ms). The virus lives symbiotically (without damage) in diploid somatic cells, but it kills the haploid pollen cells. According to this theory, restorers are modifier genes that confer virus resistance on pollen of the susceptible *ms ms* genotype. Further consideration of the very intriguing subject of cytoplasmic factors is given by John L. Jinks in *Extrachromosomal Inheritance* in this series.

Genetic load and balanced lethality

The presence of lethal and other subvital genes is referred to as the genetic load of an individual or population. As early as 1924 H. K. Hayes and H. E. Brewbaker expressed surprise at the very high genetic load among varieties of corn. Seedling lethals, largely chlorophyll deficiencies, segregated from as many as 40 per cent of the plants in the varieties tested by Brewbaker. There appeared to be no reason why lethals of this type would survive, much less accumulate, in corn. Similarly, the genetic loads of organisms such as *Drosophila* have proved to be greater than would be expected on the basis of natural mutation rates. Between 50 and 75 per cent of the chromosomes in natural populations of *Drosophila* carry one or more deleterious factors, of which half are obligate recessive lethals. The genetic load of several higher animals, including man, is equivalent to from five to ten mutations that are lethal or sublethal when homozygous.

It is evident that lethals are often maintained at high frequencies in natural populations through one or another genetic mechanism. Balanced lethality, the most important of these mechanisms, represents a special case of linkage, in which recessive lethals are linked in a state of permanent heterozygosity. In the simplest case, let us imagine two linked, recessive lethal factors, l_1 and l_2, in the heterozygote

$$\frac{L_1 \quad l_2}{l_1 \quad L_2}$$

Although phenotypically normal, heterozygotes of this type would segregate lethals when crossed. If the two loci were linked very closely, the lethal segregants from a cross of two heterozygotes like the one diagrammed above would approach very closely the following ratio.

$$\frac{1}{4}\frac{l_1\,L_2}{l_1\,L_2} : \frac{1}{2}\frac{l_1\,L_2}{L_1\,l_2} : \frac{1}{4}\frac{L_1\,l_2}{L_1\,l_2}$$

This is, in effect, a balanced lethal state in which all living individuals are of the same heterozygous genotype as their parents. The balanced lethal state is also spoken of as a state of complementarity, in which vital alleles at different loci (L_1 and L_2 in our example) complement each other to permit survival. In natural populations, lethals rarely would be expected to arise with complete linkage. Lethals that occur some distance apart along the chromosome, however, may be effectively linked by inversions. The effect of an inversion is to suppress crossing over between genes in the inverted segment. Thus no matter how distant the loci (L_1 and L_2) might be in the model above, the inversion heterozygote $L_1\ l_2/l_1\ L_2$ would act as though the loci were adjacent.

You may notice that the term *gene* has been avoided almost entirely in this discussion of lethal factors. Most lethal factors have proved not to be mutant genes, but to be deletions or cytological losses of vital gene loci. In studies of 33 naturally occurring X-chromosome lethals in *Drosophila*, for example, Milislav Demerec found that 9 were deficient for one chromosome band (the smallest cytologically defined unit), 2 were deficient for 2 bands, 3 for 3 bands, and the remainder were deficient for longer regions, including as many as 50 of the 1,000 or more in the X chromosome. Deletions that are cytologically visible in *Drosophila*, tomatoes, corn, and many other diploid organisms have proved almost invariably to be lethal to zygotes or gametes.

Gene location

With rare exceptions, genes occupy specific locations in specific chromosomes in specific genomes. Genes located in the same chromosome are linked, and their segregations are not independent but are influenced in proportion to the degree of their linkage with each other. That genes located in the same genome are allied by descent introduces the important dimension of evolution to our subject of gene location and discontinuous genetic variation.

The distances between genes, or their degree of linkage, often can be determined precisely. Linkage is expressed in terms of the frequency of crossing over between linked loci. Chromosomes range up to 350 crossover units in over-all length, commonly averaging less than 100 units. The loci of genes, centromeres, and aberration breakage points have been combined to produce detailed chromosome maps for many plant and some animal species. Over 500 genes have been located in corn, which has ten linkage groups representing the ten chromosome pairs (see Fig. 3.5).

A reduction in segregation rates occurs whenever genes are closely linked. This may pose important problems to breeders, since genetic advance through selection is greatest when loci segregate independently. The linkage of desirable and undesirable genes often is encountered in programs of gene transfer or substitution. When crosses were first made in order to transfer resistance to tobacco mosaic virus (TMV) from *Nicotiana glutinosa* to the commercial *N. tabacum*, for example, resistant selections were found to be susceptible to sun scald. Tests revealed that a locus governing susceptibility to sun scald was very closely linked to the TMV-resistant locus.

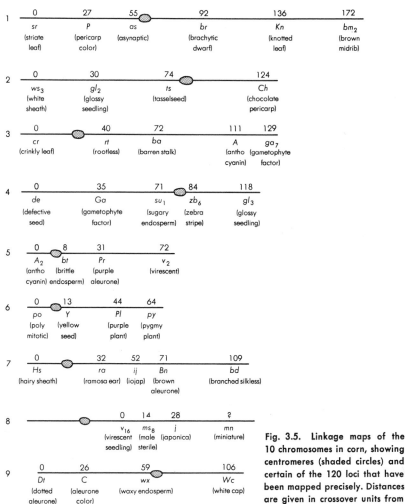

Fig. 3.5. Linkage maps of the 10 chromosomes in corn, showing centromeres (shaded circles) and certain of the 120 loci that have been mapped precisely. Distances are given in crossover units from a locus that is terminal genetically (or, in the case of chromosome 9, cytologically terminal as well).

One of the consequences of evolution is that genomes of related species have many genes in common. We should not be surprised that chimpanzees have O and A blood types, or that orangutans have A, B, and AB types, all of which are biochemically identical to those of man. N. I. Vavilov framed this type of genetic relationship as a law of homologous variation, which stated that similar genetic variations prevail among related species, but are uncommon among widely distinct species. Vavilov stressed that many genes in related species were identical, that they mutated to identical alleles, and that they were often found in similar linkage relationships with other loci.

The comparative genetics of animal coat color provides one of the

best examples of homologous variation. All mammals in an undomesti-
cated state have in common several basic color genes, appropriately
designated A, B, C, D and E. The allele A produces a mottled or
agouti pattern that confers a protective coloration. During domestication, man has selected animals of the genotype aa, with solid coat
colors. The allele B produces a black coat and the allele b a brown
coat in the respective homozygotes. The C locus is represented by multiple alleles of which the c_a allele confers the well-known albino condition on homozygotes. The D locus acts as a dilution factor; for example, white sheep are DD, black sheep, dd. Dd heterozygotes are intermediate in color, as the palomino and buckskin horses. The E locus is
an extender or intensifier of color. Genotypes resulting from combinations of these loci were first detailed by W. E. Castle in rabbits and
guinea pigs, and have been studied more recently in mammals as
diverse as cats, dogs, cattle, and pigs. Multiple alleles of the C locus
have been the subject of intensive comparative genetic studies by
L. C. Dunn and Hans Nachtsheim (Fig. 3.6). Seven alleles of this locus

Allele	Phenotype	Rabbit	Guinea pig	Dog	Cat	Rat	Mouse
C	Full color	+	+	+	+	+	+
c^d	Dark chinchilla	+	+	0	0	0	+
c^{ch}	Chinchilla	+	0	+	+	0	+
c^l	Light chinchilla	+	+	0	+	0	0
c^r	Extreme dilution	0	+	+	0	+	+
c^h	Himalayan	+	+	0	+	0	+
c^a	Albino	+	+	+	0	+	+

**Fig. 3.6.   The distribution of alleles of the albino locus in assorted mammals.
Based on experiments of Hans Nachtsheim.**

are present in many different animal species. The full dominance of C,
the temperature sensitivity of c^l, c^r and c^h, and the completely recessive
nature of c_a in all species further emphasize the homologies of this
genetic variation. The C loci are located similarly with respect to other
loci in various species. For example, the C locus is linked about twenty
units from homologous loci causing pinkeye in both mice and rats.
The homologous variation in related wheat species was studied intensively by N. I. Vavilov, who emphasized the importance of homologies as a predictive tool of the breeder. As increasing use has been
made of interspecific hybridization for the transfer of desirable genes
in plant improvement, the concept of homologous variation has often
been a useful guide to the breeder in locating and using desirable
genes.

Threshold characters

Threshold characters are traits whose segregating distributions are discontinuous but whose inheritance is multigenic. Among the best known examples is resistance to disease, in which one can often classify individuals into only two classes—resistant and alive or susceptible and dead. Several or many genes may contribute to the distinction between dead and alive, in which case survival may represent a threshold in gene action, requiring a certain number or proportion of the active alleles. Thresholds are often influenced impressively by environment.

Threshold characters that segregate into two classes are called all-or-none traits. An all-or-none trait in mice known as careener affects the animal's locomotion center and balance. Careeners wander about, often in circles, their heads tilted, their tails usually swinging vigorously back and forth. Crosses by Hans Gruneberg among careeners and normal animals in the same inbred line of mice produced the following segregations.

$$\text{careener} \times \text{careener} \rightarrow 45\% \text{ careener}$$
$$\text{careener} \times \text{normal} \ \ \rightarrow 34\% \text{ careener}$$
$$\text{normal} \ \ \times \text{normal} \ \ \rightarrow 27\% \text{ careener}$$

When careeners were crossed to unrelated, normal animals, however, none of the hybrids careened; crosses among these hybrid animals yielded fewer than 4 per cent careeners. In order to define more precisely the inheritance of careener, normal F_1 and backcross individuals were crossed to careeners with the following results.

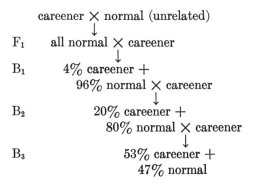

The data could not be interpreted on the basis of one or a few loci. It was concluded that many genes influenced locomotion center in mice and that careening represented the cumulative action of mutant alleles at a certain threshold number of these loci. The threshold concept was first introduced by Sewall Wright to explain similar results with polydactyly (extra toes) in guinea pigs. Subsequent studies of hereditary tumors, short tails, and number of teeth in mice have been similarly interpreted.

Threshold characters may segregate into many discontinuous classes. The number of toes, teeth, or vertebras in an animal represent this type of character. Similarly, the number of rows on ears of corn may be 8, 10, 12, 14, and so on, reflecting the paired nature of female flowers in the ear. When eight-rowed and sixteen-rowed varieties are crossed, the F_1 hybrids average twelve rows, but a continuous variation from eight rows to sixteen rows is observed in the F_2. For any plant the number of rows per ear is a function of the threshold of genes acting under a certain set of environmental conditions.

Most traits in multicellular plants and animals result from the action and interaction of many loci. Discontinuous variation is observed when one or only a few of these loci are segregating. Discontinuous segregations may also be observed when many genes are segregating, but only when threshold effects occur. Continuous variation usually arises when many genes are segregating, particularly when environmental variation obscures our ability to distinguish individual phenotypes. It is to this complex and intriguing subject that we now turn.

References

Hadorn, Ernst, *Developmental Genetics and Lethal Factors*. New York: John Wiley & Sons, Inc., 1961. A comprehensive treatment of this subject.

Hartman, Philip E., and Sigmund R. Suskind, *Gene Action*. Englewood Cliffs, N.J.: Prentice-Hall, Inc., 1964. For details of the biochemistry of gene actions and interactions.

Peters, J. A., ed., *Classic Papers in Genetics*. Englewood Cliffs, N.J.: Prentice-Hall, Inc., 1959. See especially the papers by Sewall Wright and L. C. Dunn on coat color inheritance in mammals, and that by William Bateson and R. C. Punnett on gene interactions.

Problems

3.1. Assuming the cross of $A_0A_1B_0B_1$ with $A_0A_0B_0B_0$, what phenotypic ratios will occur among the offspring if alleles with subscript 1 are (a) dominant, duplicate factors? (b) dominant, complementary factors? (c) nondominant, noninteracting factors?

3.2. In chickens the gene C is required for color in feathers; cc birds are always white. Barring of feathers is determined by a dominant sex-linked factor, and females are heterogametic. The cross of a white hen and a barred cock produced only barred chicks. If these chicks were left to interbreed, what phenotypic segregation would you expect among their offspring?

3.3. By crossing two spotted Dalmatians, a dog fancier obtained 4 spotted pups like their parents, 3 nonspotted, and 2 "Harlequin" pups that were spotted heavily and rather deaf and blind. One of the Harlequin dogs mated with a neighbor's nonspotted mongrel, and all their pups were spotted. Can the fancier obtain a breed of spotted dogs that won't segregate Harlequins?

3.4. A cytosterile corn inbred of the genotype $S\ ms\ ms\ r_{f1}\ r_{f1}$ is crossed with an inbred of the genotype $N\ Ms\ Ms\ r_{f1}\ r_{f1}$ and their hybrids are crossed with a restorer hybrid of the genotype $N\ Ms\ ms\ R_{f1}\ r_{f1}$ to produce the commercial doublecross seeds. What proportion of the plants among doublecross hybrids will be cytosterile?

3.5. What possible interpretations can you suggest for the fact that albino cats (see Fig. 3.6) have not been discovered?

Continuous Variation

Over forty-three million different genotypes can segregate from a cross involving sixteen heterozygous loci. This is a sobering thought to the geneticist who deals with economic traits like yield or growth rate—traits for which segregations rarely involve as few as sixteen segregating loci. Quantitative genetics deals with those characters for which phenotypic variation is continuous rather than discontinuous, for which genetic differences are of degree rather than of kind. Most economically important traits fall into this category. The breeder's search for outstanding phenotypes inevitably must be tempered with the cold, hard facts about these quantitative traits: first, that they commonly result from the action of many genes, second, that they commonly are greatly influenced by environmental variations; finally, that the genes favorably influencing an economic trait often occur in linkage groups with undesirable neighbors.

The basic statistical theory for continuous genetic variation was developed almost forty years ago by R. A. Fisher, Sewall Wright, and J. B. S. Haldane. Statistical theories permit us to predict the genetic behavior of model populations, in which genes act in a specified manner. Complicating factors to be considered in devising these model populations include dominance, non-allelic interactions, multiplicative gene action and linkage. By comparing a model population with experimental populations we should be able to decide whether genes are acting as predicted, and to plan economic methods for putting these genes to work. There are, then, two major aspects of quantitative genetic inquiry—one, observational or experimental, the other, predictive or theoretical. Not entirely unlike other sciences, the theoretical aspects of the science of quantitative genetics, largely beyond the scope of this book, have run well ahead of the experimental aspects.

Metrical traits

Traits that show continuous phenotypic variation are referred to as metrical traits, because their study depends upon measurements rather than upon counts. Since small single progenies rarely suffice for their genetic analysis, populations comprising many progenies must be used. Thus the analysis of quantitative genetic variation must incorporate the fundamental aspects of population genetics, considered in detail in the companion text in this series by Lawrence F. Mettler, *Population Genetics and Evolution.*

Metrical traits almost inevitably show, upon analysis, a large environmental component of variation. As this environmental component increases, even the most discrete genetic differences can be obscured. The effect of environmental variation on a monogenic segregation in tomatoes is illustrated in Fig. 4.1. The length of hypocotyl (stem of a seedling) varies greatly in different tomato varieties, although only slight variation occurs within varieties. Tomatoes are self-fertilized and the parent lines chosen for this study showed no genetic variation in hypocotyl lengths. The first generation or F_1 hybrids were quite comparable to the long hypocotyl parent both in mean and phenotypic variance. When F_1 plants were self-fertilized to produce the second or F_2 generation, and backcrossed to the short hypocotyl parent, the bimodal (two-peaked) distributions of Fig. 4.1 were obtained. The two peaks obtained in each segregating population corresponded closely to the peaks of the two parental distributions. The data can best be interpreted by assuming that the difference in hypocotyl length between the two varieties is governed by a single locus, D/d, with dominance of the allele contributed by the long hypocotyl parent. Other studies support fully this conclusion, demonstrating heritability for hypocotyl length to be about 50 per cent, i.e., the environmental variance about equals the additive genetic variance. If heritability were less than 25 per cent, we could no longer distinguish this clearly as a monogenic segregation, since the bimodality disappears, and evidence regarding dominance of the long hypocotyl would be, at best, debatable. These data illustrate for us the narrow bridge between dis-

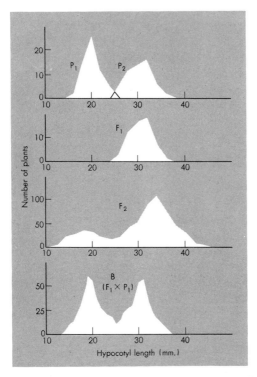

Fig. 4.1. Segregations for hypocotyl length in tomato seedlings.
Distributions indicate monogenic
control with appreciable environmental variance. Based on experiments of E. Weber.

continuous and continuous genetic variation, and the importance of
environment to this distinction. When the difference between genotypes is an extra egg or an additional pound of steak per month, even
the most desultory of environmental changes—disease, nutrition,
weather—can obscure genetic differences.

J. G. Koelreuter, one of the earliest of plant hybridizers, studied
continuous variation among segregating progenies of tobacco as early
as 1760. Koelreuter crossed species of tobacco that differed greatly in
flower size and other traits. The F_1 hybrids were commonly intermediate to their parents and were more or less uniform. In contrast
the F_2 plants obtained by self-fertilizing the F_1 hybrids varied greatly,
often ranging from one parental extreme to the other. Hybridizers in
the following century verified these observations in many cultigens.
Mendel had the insight to select carefully seven traits in peas in
which this type of continuous variation among F_2 plants did not occur.
One trait studied by Mendel, however, was a metrical. A dwarf mutant
strain of peas that rarely exceeded one foot in height was crossed with
plants that grew about six feet high on trellises. The F_1 hybrids were
similar to the tall parent and the F_2 segregated **787** tall and **277** short
plants (Mendel took care to grow the plants to maturity in similar

soils, with similar watering schedules, disregarding diseased plants, and so on). Genes of this type have a major effect on a metrical trait, that is, an effect so great that random variations or environmental effects are insignificant by comparison. It became apparent in the studies of Johannsen (see Chapter 1) that the phenotypic variation of metrical traits often included a large nongenetic component. Control or estimation of this component was necessary in order to outline clearly the genetic segregations involved. It remained for Hermann Nilsson-Ehle and E. M. East to propose independently a theory that linked Mendelian factors with the continuous variations of metrical traits.

Polygenes

Nilsson-Ehle studied the segregations of red color in the seeds and floral parts of common bread wheats. In 1906 crosses were made between plants differing in glume (floral part) color, one parent having red-brown glumes, the other having colorless glumes. The F_1 plants were found to have red-brown glumes. The F_2 families segregated 1,410 red-glumed and only 94 colorless-glumed plants, clearly discrepant from a monogenic ratio. They fit very well a 15:1 ratio, however, which could be expected on the assumption that two identical genes governed glume color, with only the homozygous recessive genotype being colorless. These discontinuous genetic variations served as a clue to Nilsson-Ehle in his interpretation of data from his concurrent studies of the continuous genetic variation in seed colors. When varieties with red seeds were crossed with white-seeded lines, the F_1 hybrids produced dilute red seeds intermediate in color between the parents. In the F_2 families, pigment intensity varied continuously from deep red to colorless, with most seeds in the intermediate or dilute red class. Only those seeds that were completely colorless could be distinguished with ease. In most crosses, approximately $\frac{1}{16}$ of the F_2 plants were of this class.

Nilsson-Ehle concluded that duplicate factors accounted for the redness of seeds, as they did for the glume colors. The intermediacy of seed color in F_1 plants and the continuous variation in pigmentation of red F_2 seeds, however, were considered to result from the cumulative action, without dominance, of the duplicate, pigment-producing alleles (Fig. 4.2). We see that the 15:1 segregation was considered to reflect a combination of phenotypes from 1:4:6:4:1 distribution, calculated on the basis of duplicate, nondominant genes, rather than from a 9:3:3:1 distribution (for which dominance is assumed). In still other crosses, the colorless seeded plants comprised only $\frac{1}{64}$ of the F_2 popu-

Parents: White $(A_0A_0B_0B_0)$ × Dark red $(A_1A_1B_1B_1)$
F_1: Medium red $(A_0A_1B_0B_1)$

F_2: Genotypes	Phenotypes	Phenotypic summaries
$\frac{1}{16}A_0A_0B_0B_0$	White	$\frac{1}{16}$ White
$\frac{2}{16}A_0A_0B_0B_1$	Light red	
$\frac{1}{16}A_0A_0B_1B_1$	Medium red	
$\frac{2}{16}A_0A_1B_0B_0$	Light red	$\frac{4}{16}$ Light red
$\frac{4}{16}A_0A_1B_0B_1$	Medium red	$\frac{6}{16}$ Medium red
$\frac{2}{16}A_0A_1B_1B_1$	Red	$\frac{4}{16}$ Red
$\frac{1}{16}A_1A_1B_0B_0$	Medium red	$\frac{1}{16}$ Dark red
$\frac{2}{16}A_1A_1B_0B_1$	Red	
$\frac{1}{16}A_1A_1B_1B_1$	Dark red	

$\frac{15}{16}$ Red (All shades)

Fig. 4.2. F_2 segregations for wheat seed colors governed by duplicate genes acting without dominance. Based on experiments of Hermann Nilsson-Ehle.

lation, and a third locus affecting redness in the same quantitative fashion was postulated by Nilsson-Ehle.

The interpretation of Nilsson-Ehle's data led to the proposal that genetic factors whose individual effects were equivalent, but whose actions intensified each other, be termed *polymeric genes* (or *multiple factors*). Also used somewhat interchangeably with these terms is *polygene,* coined by Kenneth Mather. Mather proposed that polygenes could be distinguished from major genes not only by their minor and cumulative action, but also by their chromosomal location in linked blocks. This important theory is acknowleged to hold for only a small proportion of polymeric genes.[1]

Conclusive evidence for polygenic systems was obtained from studies of metrical traits in corn and tobacco started by E. M. East in 1905. Ear lengths were studied in corn, following crosses of two varieties that differed almost threefold (66 mm. vs. 168 mm.) with respect to this trait. Similarly, flower lengths were investigated in progeny of two tobacco lines with flowers differing twofold in length (40 mm. vs. 93 mm.). The classic data of R. A. Emerson and East on the corn ear lengths, based on the cross of Tom Thumb and Black Mexican varieties, are given in Fig. 4.3. The F_1 hybrids averaged about midway between their parents. Similarly, the averages of segregating F_2 populations (derived by self-pollination of the F_1 plants) fell about midway between the original parents. While the F_1 plants were more or less uniform, the F_2 plants showed great variation, ranging continuously in length almost from one parental extreme to the other. Although the F_2 populations grown by East were very large, few of the F_2 plants equaled the extreme expressions of the parents, and none exceeded these extremes. Each of the populations was distributed symmetrically

[1] See I. M. Lerner, *Genetic Basis for Selection* (Wiley, 1956), chap. 2.

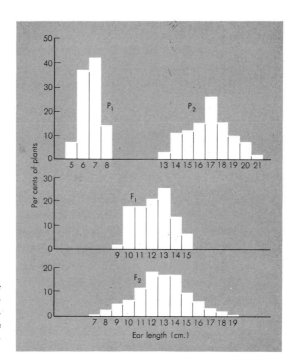

Fig. 4.3. Inheritance of a metrical trait in corn. Distributions of ear lengths are shown for the varieties Tom Thumb (P_1), Black Mexican (P_2), and their F_1 and F_2 progeny. Based on experiments of E. M. East.

or normally about its mean. If the F_1 were crossed back to the Tom Thumb parent, what might the average ear length have been in B_1?

East's observations of flower lengths in self-pollinated tobacco were comparable to those he obtained with cross-pollinated corn. The average flower lengths of F_1 and F_2 populations (64 mm. and 68 mm., respectively) fell midway between the parental values of 40 mm. and 93 mm. East continued the tobacco studies into advanced progenies, establishing F_3, F_4, and other advanced lines by continued self-pollination. Some of these advanced inbred generations are diagrammed in Fig. 4.4, together with the F_2 population. The advanced families differed greatly in average performances, ranging from one parental extreme to the other. The F_2 population, however, showed the greatest variation about the mean. The variation of advanced progenies gradually decreased upon inbreeding. This was interpreted to indicate a slow approach to homozygosity for the genes influencing flower length. An important fact emerging from studies of advanced lines was that much genetic variability remained even after several generations of inbreeding. By selecting large flowered and small flowered segregants in the F_4 generation, for example, East was able to establish F_5 lines that differed significantly in flower lengths, in contrast to Johannsen's selections in beans (see Fig. 1.4). This indicates a long continued genetic segregation of genes influencing flower length. The data could not be accounted for on the basis of one, or even of a few, gene loci; a minimum estimate of four loci was given.

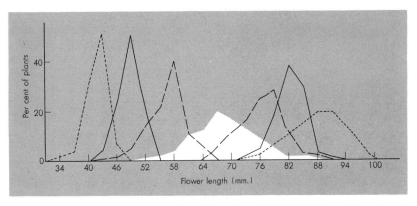

Fig. 4.4. Frequency distributions of tobacco flower lengths in F_2 (white) and six advanced progeny obtained by self-pollination. Original parents averaged 40 mm. and 93 mm. in length. Based on experiments of E. M. East.

Emerson and East devised a theoretical model to clarify their concept of the multiple factors influencing flower and ear lengths. Two parent plants were postulated to be 12 inches and 28 inches tall. On the assumption that the difference of 16 inches between these parents was based on a single allelic pair acting without dominance, the F_1 plants average 20 inches in height and the F_2 plants should segregate

$$\frac{1}{4} A_0 A_0 = 12 \text{ inches}$$
$$\frac{1}{2} A_0 A_1 = 20 \text{ inches}$$
$$\frac{1}{4} A_1 A_1 = 28 \text{ inches}$$

Each A_1 allele is assumed on this basis to contribute 8 inches to height. This must not be interpreted to mean that, since $A_0 A_0$ plants are 12 inches high, each A_0 allele is contributing 6 inches to height! It is clear, rather, that A_0 alleles *plus* the entire residual genotype account for this remaining 12 inches. We shall refer to alleles such as A_1 in this model as active alleles. We can make no statements about the activity of the A_0 allele other than that it does not contribute a measurable increment to height in the segregating families.

Emerson and East first altered this one-locus model to assume two allelic pairs, with dominance again absent. On this basis, the F_2 segregation involves five phenotypes:

12 inches $= A_0 A_0 B_0 B_0$
16 inches $= A_0 A_0 B_0 B_1$ and $A_0 A_1 B_0 B_0$
20 inches $= A_0 A_0 B_1 B_1$ and $A_0 A_1 B_0 B_1$ and $A_1 A_1 B_0 B_0$
24 inches $= A_1 A_1 B_1 B_0$ and $A_0 A_1 B_1 B_1$
28 inches $= A_1 A_1 B_1 B_1$

The F_2 phenotypic segregation would be in a ratio of 1:4:6:4:1, with each active allele (A_1 or B_1) viewed as contributing 4 inches to height.

When the model is changed to assume four allelic pairs, each active allele contributes 2 inches to height, and so forth. Note that the expectations in these examples are based on the purely additive action of the active alleles, with no dominance and no interactions between loci. These are complications reserved for later sections.

The segregations with increasing numbers of allelic pairs follow the expansion of the binomial $(a + b)^n$, where $n =$ the number of segregating alleles. In the one-gene model, $n = 2$, and

$$(a + b)^2 = a^2 + 2ab + b^2$$

Letting a represent the allele A_0, and b the active allele A_1, this formula represents in a mathematical way the familiar ratio

$$\tfrac{1}{4} A_0A_0 : \tfrac{1}{2} A_0A_1 : \tfrac{1}{4} A_1A_1$$

In a similar manner, the binomial expansion for the two-locus model is

$$(a + b)^4 = a^4 + 4a^3b + 6a^2b^2 + 4ab^3 + b^4$$

Letting a represent null alleles like A_0 and B_0 and b represent active alleles like A_1 and B_1, this expansion can be seen to represent an F_2 segregation of 1:4:6:4:1.

Phenotype frequency	Number of alleles	
	Null	Active
$\frac{1}{16}$	4	0
$\frac{4}{16}$	3	1
$\frac{6}{16}$	2	2
$\frac{4}{16}$	1	3
$\frac{1}{16}$	0	4

The phenotypic frequencies are derived directly from the coefficients (1,4,6, etc.) of the terms obtained upon expansion of the binomial. Thus $4a^2b^2$ has a frequency of 4 out of the total 16; this total can be obtained by squaring the number (n) of segregating alleles.

The numbers of active alleles in the preceding table represent the powers to which b is raised in successive terms of the binomial. Similarly, the frequencies of the null alleles (A_0, B_0) are represented by the powers to which a is raised. With increasing numbers of segregating loci, the expansion of the binomial produces a frequency pyramid of F_2 segregations, illustrated below.

1 locus				$\frac{1}{4}$	$\frac{2}{4}$	$\frac{1}{4}$			
2 loci			$\frac{1}{16}$	$\frac{4}{16}$	$\frac{6}{16}$	$\frac{4}{16}$	$\frac{1}{16}$		
3 loci		$\frac{1}{64}$	$\frac{6}{64}$	$\frac{15}{64}$	$\frac{20}{64}$	$\frac{15}{64}$	$\frac{6}{64}$	$\frac{1}{64}$	
4 loci	$\frac{1}{256}$	$\frac{8}{256}$	$\frac{28}{256}$	$\frac{56}{256}$	$\frac{70}{256}$	$\frac{56}{256}$	$\frac{28}{256}$	$\frac{8}{256}$	$\frac{1}{256}$

The binomial expansion for a hypothetical population (F_2) involving an infinite number of loci acting without dominance produces the normal probability distribution.

The consequences of increasing gene number in the binomial model satisfactorily support many of the observations of Emerson and East. As the number of gene pairs increases, the contribution of each gene becomes correspondingly less, and the number of expected genotypes increases. With increasing gene number, we may expect the long continued segregations observed by East, as well as the stabilization, upon continued inbreeding, of advanced progenies at mean values ranging from one parental extreme to the other.

Calculations of the number of segregating gene pairs may be made with reference to the binomial model. As the number of segregating gene pairs (n) increases, the frequency of the extreme phenotypes decreases. The expected frequency of any extreme phenotype is obtained simply by $(\frac{1}{2})^{2n}$. For $n = 5$ gene pairs, this frequency equals 1 out of 1,024, for 10 gene pairs, 1 out of 1,048,576. The frequency of extreme phenotypes thus gives an estimate of the number of segregating gene loci. A more accurate statistical estimate of polymeric gene number for a segregating trait may be made by comparing the obtained frequencies of all genotypes with frequencies estimated from theoretical binomial distributions.

The extreme phenotypes in a segregating population often exceed those of the parent lines. Varieties of rice that mature in about one hundred days may, when crossed, produce F_2 and advanced lines differing by as much as forty days in maturity. Segregants like these, which exceed their parental averages, are referred to as transgressive segregants. This type of segregation illustrates an important consequence of polygenic action, namely, that many different genotypes may produce the same phenotype.

The simple polygenic model of Emerson and East has produced surprisingly good approximations of actual results of a great many studies of metrical traits such as egg production in chickens, plant height, and the productivity of silkworms. It was not long after the studies of Emerson and East, however, that observations were made that were inconsistent with their model. The intentional oversimplification of this, as well as all models, did not take into account the fact that polygenes, like other genes, occasionally showed dominance, interacted with one another or with the ever present environment, or simply acted unpredictably. Increasingly complex models have been constructed by the biometrician, therefore, to accommodate new complications in polygene action. We shall now turn to an examination of some of these complications.

Dominance and nonallelic gene interaction

Interactions among polygenes are of two types: dominance interaction (between alleles) and nonallelic interaction. Statistically, these interactions may be expressed as components of genetic variance, V_G (see Chapter 1). For any metrical trait, then, there are six components of variance.

V_P	Phenotypic	V_A	Additive
V_E	Environmental	V_D	Dominance
V_G	Genetic	V_N	Nonallelic

Phenotypic variance of a trait may first be divided into its genetic and environmental components, V_G and V_E. When an experiment is designed accordingly, genetic variance may be further subdivided into its additive, dominance, and nonallelic components, and the phenotypic variance expressed as

$$V_P = V_A + V_D + V_N + V_E$$

In the absence of dominance and nonallelic interactions, the genetic variance is entirely additive. Any two alleles that have different quantitative effects contribute V_A. *Additive genetic variance is the chief cause of resemblance among parents and offspring*, and it commonly exceeds greatly the dominance and nonallelic variances. When dominance occurs, two alleles affecting a metrical trait contribute both V_A and V_D.

Variance components may be calculated in several different ways, each calling for care in the design of the experiment and the choice of material. A critical estimate of environmental variance must be made (see Chapter 1), and the genetic variance of segregating populations obtained by subtraction, $V_G = V_P - V_E$. This may also be achieved by the factorial analysis of variance components, in which parents are crossed, and the F_1, F_2, and backcross populations are analyzed. An experimental technique referred to as diallel analysis also increases the precision of variance analyses. For diallel analysis, several individuals differing in a metrical trait are intercrossed in all combinations, and all the progenies are studied.

Dominance variance

The dominance component of variance represents statistically those deviations of a heterozygous hybrid from the midpoint between its homozygous parents. Dominance is illustrated at the top of the following page on a scale for a single pair of alleles, A_0 and A_1.

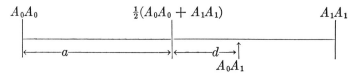

In this illustration, the heterozygote A_0A_1 is pictured as more like parent A_1A_1 than parent A_0A_0. The dominance deviation of the heterozygote from the midparental point is symbolized as d. The difference between the homozygous parents equals $a + a$ or $2a$. When $d = 0$, dominance is absent and the genetic variance is wholly additive (as we assumed in the model of Emerson and East). When $d = a$, dominance is complete.

For genetic traits under the control of many genes, dominance variance is the summation of the individual dominance components, or $\Sigma\, d$. If we supposed four gene pairs to govern a trait, with full dominance $(d = a)$ for two pairs and no dominance $(d = 0)$ for the other two pairs, the over-all dominance effect on mean values would appear as $d = \frac{1}{2}a$, or as partial dominance. Similarly, we should note that dominance may occur in a minus as well as a plus direction, so that the over-all effect of summation may even be the apparent absence of dominance.

Additive and dominance components of variance are expressed in terms of the squares of a and d. In an F_2 progeny segregating from a single cross, phenotypic variance is represented by

$$V_P \text{ (of } F_2) = \tfrac{1}{2}a^2 + \tfrac{1}{4}d^2 + V_E$$

where $\frac{1}{2}a^2$ represents the contribution of additive genetic variance in the F_2 population, $\frac{1}{4}d^2$ represents the dominance component, and V_E the environmental component (nonallelic interactions are assumed not to occur). Similarly, the phenotypic variance of a backcross population is represented by

$$V_P \text{ (of B)} = \tfrac{1}{4}a^2 + \tfrac{1}{4}d^2 + V_E$$

It is not within the scope of this book to derive these equations, but they are obtained by consideration of the binomial expansion.

The use of variance components in the calculation of dominance and heritability effects is illustrated in Fig. 4.5. In this study, partial dominance was indicated for genes governing earliness in flowering in segregating progenies of the wheat varieties Ramona and Baart. The partial dominance of earliness appeared as a deviation of the F_1 hybrids from the midparental point toward the mean of the early flowering parent. Partial dominance also is indicated by the large dominance variance derived from the statistical analysis. Dominance interaction accounted here for almost 25 per cent of the total genetic variance.

Generation	Mean	Phenotypic variance
P_1 (Ramona)	13.0	11.04
P_2 (Baart)	27.6	10.32
F_1	18.5	5.24
F_2	21.2	40.35
B_1	15.6	17.35
B_2	23.4	34.29

(1) Phenotypic variance of $F_2 = \frac{1}{2}a^2 + \frac{1}{4}d^2 + V_E = 40.35$

(2) Average variance of $B = \frac{1}{4}a^2 + \frac{1}{4}d^2 + V_E = \frac{17.35 + 34.29}{2} = 25.82$

(3) $(1) - (2) = \frac{1}{4}a^2 = 14.53$; $a^2 = 58.12$

(4) V_E = average of V_P's for $P_1 + P_2 + F_1 = \frac{11.04 + 10.32 + 5.24}{3} = 8.89$

(5) Using the values for the F_2 population,
$V_P = V_A + V_D + V_E$
or $V_D = V_P - V_A - V_E$
But since $V_P = 40.35$, $V_A = \frac{1}{2}a^2 = 29.06$, and $V_E = 8.89$,
V_D (by subtraction) $= 9.58$

(6) Degree of dominance $= \frac{d}{a} = \frac{\sqrt{4 V_D}}{\sqrt{2 V_A}} = \frac{\sqrt{38.3}}{\sqrt{58.1}} = 0.8$

(7) Heritability $= \frac{V_A}{V_P} = \frac{29.06}{40.35} = 72\%$

Fig. 4.5. Calculations illustrating the application of variance components to analyses of wheat heading dates (calculated from an arbitrary starting date) from a cross of the varieties Ramona and Baart. Based on experiments of R. W. Allard.

The degree of dominance is expressed as d/a, which equals one, as we have noted, when $d = a$ ("complete" dominance). In the example in Fig. 4.5, the degree of dominance is 0.57.

Dominance has been shown to contribute a significant component to variances of a wide variety of metrical traits. As we shall see in the following chapter, dominance provides the most plausible basis for heterosis and inbreeding depression. Studies of field corn, for example, indicate a significant dominance component in the inheritance of seed yield, diameter of ear, and length of ear husk, while genetic variance appears to be entirely additive for traits such as plant height or ear length. It should be observed that conclusions such as these apply specifically to the segregating populations that have been measured. Other crosses within the same or other species would not necessarily involve the same segregating loci, and might lead to different conclusions regarding dominance.

Nonallelic interaction variance

Nonallelic gene interactions exist as a complication in the analysis of quantitative inheritance, and their role is difficult to assess. Nonallelic interactions are common among genes governing discontinuously-segregating traits, and this has led to the inference that they should also be common for continuously varying traits. It is probable, however, that only rarely are they large enough to constitute a serious error in calculation if neglected. Nonallelic interaction is also referred to as epistatic interaction, or simply as interaction variance. Nonallelic interaction variance, however, represents statistical, not always genic epistasis. It includes interactions between additive values of different loci, interactions between additive and dominance contributions, and interactions between the dominance contributions. Further subdivisions of interaction variance are made according to the number of loci involved; these higher order interactions contribute so little variance that they are usually ignored in analyses.

The conventional genetic model for nonallelic gene interactions is that of epistasis. The complementary and duplicate factor forms of epistasis each may contribute significant dominance (V_D) as well as nonallelic (V_N) components to genetic variance. As an example, the complementary model was illustrated in Chapter 3 by synthetic pathways catalyzed at successive steps by enzymes governed by different genes.

$$P_1 \xrightarrow{\text{gene } A_1} P_2 \xrightarrow{\text{gene } B_1} P_3 \xrightarrow{\text{gene } C_1} P_4 \ldots$$

When the final enzymatic product of such a pathway is one of the several products contributing to a metrical trait, the interaction of active alleles A_1, B_1, and so forth, would appear as nonallelic variance in analyses. Dominance, as of A_1 over A_0, may or may not occur.

In the study of traits such as tomato fruit weights, where almost forty controlling loci were estimated to segregate in diverse crosses, it should be apparent that any conventional genetic analysis, locus by locus, is out of the question. The biometrical approach seeks, in such a case, to discover the major components of genetic variance and to predict the genetic gains possible under this scheme.

Multiplicative gene action

When a midget cherry tomato is crossed with a large fruited commercial variety, the hybrid fruits are disappointingly small. At first encounter we might describe this simply as a case of the dominance of the small fruit. Factorial analysis of this metrical trait, however, has shown that dominance is not involved at all. The data summarized in Fig. 4.6 were derived from one such analysis by Leroy Powers of crosses between a midget tomato, Red Currant, and a large slicing tomato, Danmark. F_1 fruits had much smaller locule weights than the midparental average, and the F_2 and backcross progeny were biased toward the small fruited type.

An interpretation of the data in Fig. 4.6 was made by recognizing that fruit weight is a volumetric trait. Since volumes represent not the sum but the product of heights, widths, and depths, statistical geneticists noted that the action of genes influencing such a trait might not

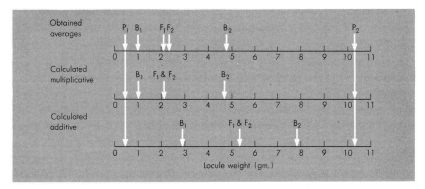

Fig. 4.6. Phenotypic effects of multiplicative gene action in tomatoes. Average locule (section) weights are shown for the parents, Red Currant (P₁) and Danmark (P₂), and for their F₁, F₂, and backcross families (B₁ = F₁ × P₁; B₂ = F₁ × P₂). Averages are calculated for the expectations of additive and multiplicative gene action. Based on experiments of LeRoy Powers.

be arithmetically additive, but multiplicative. Alleles acting to increase the length of a tomato fruit, for example, might be expected to interact with genes increasing its radius not in an additive but in a multiplicative or geometric fashion, since volume reflects the product rather than the sum of lengths and radii. Certain statistical transformations, of which the logarithmic transformation is most used, convert geometric series into additive series. Powers transformed the tomato fruit weight averages (Fig. 4.6) into logarithms. The calculated multiplicative or logarithmic averages for F_1, F_2, and backcross populations were nearly identical to those that had been obtained. The data provided convincing evidence that multiplicative gene action influenced fruit weight segregations in this series of crosses.

Additive gene action, similar to that proposed by R. A. Emerson and E. M. East, creates arithmetic series such as 3, 6, 9, 12, . . . , representing the successive contributions (plus 3, in this example) of 1, 2, 3, and 4 active alleles. In contrast, multiplicative action produces geometric series such as 3, 9, 27, 81, . . . , representing the successive contributions (times 3, in this example) of 1, 2, 3, and 4 active alleles. A more realistic example of an arithmetic phenotypic series might be 1.1, 1.2, 1.3, and 1.4, representing an additive increment of 0.1 per active allele. A more realistic example of geometric series might be 1, 1.1, 1.21, 1.331, 1.4641, . . . , representing increase by a factor of 1.1 or a multiplicative increment of 10 per cent per active allele.

One consequence of multiplicative gene action is that values in a segregating population will not follow the normal probability distribution. This is illustrated in Fig. 4.7 with the fruit-weight data of Powers. On an arithmetic scale, the distribution of fruit weights for this segre-

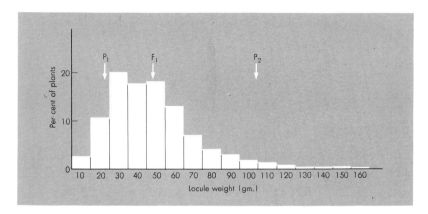

Fig. 4.7. Asymmetrical distribution of fruit locule weights from 928 tomato plants in a segregating population. Means of parents (P₁, P₂) and of the segregating population (F₁) are noted by arrows. Based on experiments of LeRoy Powers.

gating backcross family clearly was not symmetrical. The mean value was not centrally located, and the upper tail of the curve approached zero much more slowly than did the lower tail. When a logarithmic transformation of these data is made, however, the transformed data fit the normal probability curve very well. Effects like these, which disappear upon transformation, are referred to as scale effects and can be interpreted as resulting from multiplicative gene action. J. W. McArthur first demonstrated scale effects in tomatoes, later substantiating his findings in studies of the body weights of mice. McArthur emphasized that convincing evidence of multiplicative gene action is provided whenever means and variances are correlated. In the normal probability distribution, means and variances are independent; as the mean increases, the variance may increase or decrease at random. In the presence of scale effects, however, the variance becomes dependent upon the mean; that is, as means increase, so do variances. One consequence of this dependence is the constancy of coefficients of variation for segregating populations with different means, a familiar phenomenon to agricultural scientists in applied research.

Genotype-environment interaction

We have considered in this chapter two types of interactions —dominance (interallelic interaction) and nonallelic gene interactions. A third important class of interaction occurs between genes and their environment. The c^h coat-color allele provides a classic example of genotype-environment interaction. The $c^h c^h$ homozygote produces the familiar Himalayan pattern of rabbits and the Siamese pattern of cats (see Fig. 3.6). Pigment is produced only in the extremities of the $c^h c^h$ animal—tail, feet, nose, and ear tips. The tyrosinase enzyme produced by the c^h allele is temperature sensitive. Only at low body temperatures (as in an animal's extremities) is it able to catalyze the synthesis of the black melanin pigment. When a white animal having the c^h allele is shaved and ice is applied locally, for example, the hair growing into the shaved area is black. Related alleles confer the familiar winter-white, summer-dark coat patterns (pigmented hairs form during the colder months).

The differential performance of genotypes in different environments is also very familiar to geneticists. An example is that of the change in quality (sweetness, acidity) of two varieties of oranges, each a single genotype, grown at different elevations in Hawaii:

	500 feet	1,000 feet
Washington Navel	high	low
Satsuma Mandarin	low	high

In this simplest form, genotype-environment interaction involves a switch in the order of performance, in which genotype 1 is superior to genotype 2 in environment A, but inferior to it in environment B. The importance of this interaction is reflected in many of the recommendations that accompany newly released crop varieties. Varieties are recommended as superior only on certain soils, with certain fertilizer applications, or in accompaniment with other plants, and so forth.

The variance contributed by genotype-environment interactions may be calculated when the environmental factor can be controlled and applied as a treatment to different genotypes as, for example, the treatment of Washington Navel and Satsuma oranges with different levels of fertilizer or fungicide. Normally, however, the genotype-environment interaction cannot be calculated and is regarded as part of the environmental variance (V_E). Studies in poultry indicate that this type of interaction is significant only when both the genetic and environmental variances are also very large, and that it is of less importance when an experiment is conducted under uniform environmental conditions.

Complications and summary

If a tomato has twelve pairs of chromosomes and if a metrical trait like fruit weight is controlled by forty segregating loci, many of these loci must be linked. Linkage thus adds an important complication to analyses of genetic variance for metrical traits. An important effect of linkage is to bias upward the frequencies of linked gene complexes among segregating progenies. F_2 populations thus may fail to fit a normal distribution, but include nonparental (crossover) types in frequencies lower than those predicted on the basis of independent segregation. This is illustrated below for the F_2 generation from the cross, $AAbb \times aaBB$; frequencies of $aabb$ segregants are calculated for different A-B map distances:

A-B map distance	$aabb$ frequency
50 units (or more)	1/16
20 units	1/100
10 units	1/400
1 unit	1/40,000
n units	$n^2/40,000$

In some instances polygenes influencing a certain trait occur in linked clusters, but they are more commonly distributed randomly throughout the genome.

One other simplifying assumption made throughout our discussion of metrical traits has been that all polygenic loci have only two alleles. There is little doubt, however, that multiple allelism also occurs at such loci. The possibility thus arises that two parents could contribute four different alleles to their hybrids, with an attendant increase in genotypic variability among advanced generations of the cross. Analyzing the contributions of linkage and multiple allelism to continuous genetic variation is a subject left to advanced students of this subject.

Let us summarize here the salient features of continuous genetic variation. First, most metrical traits are governed by many genes, referred to as polygenes, that are in no sense mere replicas of a single locus ("multiple factors") although those governing a given trait are similar in action. Each polygene has a relatively trivial effect on phenotype. Since these individual effects are small, the effect of environment on expression of polygenes may be great. Polygenes can occur in linked complexes or blocks. They often show dominance, and probably interact in as many and as diverse ways as do the genes affecting discontinuously varying traits. Because of the high number of loci that influence most metrical traits, genetic analysis rests heavily on the biometrical approach, and genetic advance under selection often depends greatly on the precision of these variance analyses.

References

Allard, R. W., *Principles of Plant Breeding*. New York: John Wiley & Sons, Inc., 1960. Chapters 8, 9, and 10 deal readably with quantitative inheritance and variance component analyses.

Falconer, D. S., *Introduction to Quantitative Genetics*. New York: The Ronald Press Company, 1960. Chapters 6, 7, and 8 describe variance analyses for metrical traits and Chapter 17 provides details on scale effects.

Kempthorne, Oscar, *An Introduction to Genetic Statistics.* New York: John
Wiley & Sons, Inc., 1957. The biometrical treatment of continuous
variation (especially in Chapter 15) is for the student who likes
challenges.

Lerner, I. M., *Genetic Basis for Selection.* New York: John Wiley & Sons,
Inc., 1958. Chapter 2 contains an excellent treatment of the intrica-
cies of polygenic inheritance.

Problems

4.1. Considering the following hypothetical values—$V_E = 20$, $V_A = 20$,
$V_D = 15$, and $V_N = 25$—what proportion of the phenotypic variance
is genetic? What is the coefficient of heritability? What accounts
for the difference in these values?

4.2. Holstein cows produce about 12 per cent more milk than Guernseys,
while the Guernseys produce about 30 per cent higher butterfat
content. Each of these differences involves about 10 loci, acting
without dominance. What proportion of the F_2 animals from a
Guernsey-Holstein cross would produce as much milk as the Holstein yet have a butterfat percentage as high as the Guernsey?

4.3. The following mean body weights and phenotypic variances were obtained
for mature cocks in the Bantam and Plymouth Rock breeds and
their hybrids:

	Mean	Variance
Bantam	1.4#	0.1
Plymouth Rock	6.6#	0.5
F₁	3.4#	0.3
F₂	3.6#	1.2
B₁	2.5#	0.8
B₂	4.8#	1.0

Assuming the absence of nonallelic interactions, calculate the degree
of dominance and heritability of this trait. Which breed contributes
the dominant alleles?; could scale effects be implicated?

4.4. At the age of 2 months, a common laboratory strain of mice weighed 23
gm., and had a phenotypic variance of 6.55. Following many generations of inbreeding and selection, J. W. McArthur was able to isolate
a midget strain ($\bar{x} = 12$ gm., $V_P = 2.92$) and a giant strain ($\bar{x} = 40$
gm., $V_P = 26.01$). Calculate coefficients of variation and draw
conclusions.

$$\mathcal{Five}$$

Heterosis

Heterosis is a genetic expression of the beneficial effects of hybridization. It is the principal weapon in the arsenal of applied animal and plant geneticists. In view of the extent to which the vigor of hybrids has been studied, it may seem surprising that the heterosis concept, formulated a half century ago, continues to provide a wealth of intriguing genetic puzzles.

Heterosis and inbreeding depression

Inbreeding depression is the converse of heterosis. Whenever one is found, the other may confidently be expected to occur. In general terms, *the vigor lost during inbreeding tends to be restored upon crossing.* Heterosis and inbreeding depression are often dealt with in relation to characters that determine an individual's fitness, its proportionate contribution to the next generation. In this frame of reference, the fitness lost upon inbreeding tends to be restored by crossing. We have related inbreeding deterioration principally to an increase in homozygosity (Chapter 2). In contrast, hybrid vigor probably does not relate principally to the increase in heterozygosity per se.

It was through a recognition of the dramatic vigor of many plant hybrids that biologists were drawn to re-examine the basis for the depression in vigor that occurs

70

upon inbreeding. Koelreuter's critical studies of hybridization in plants (Chapter 4) were published between 1761 and 1766. Koelreuter meticulously and systematically recorded the variations among hybrids and their parents. He recorded many cases of excessive vigor of hybrids over their parents. Two observations about hybrid vigor were stressed by Koelreuter. First, since hybrid vigor was more pronounced among distantly related plants than it was among those closely allied, Koelreuter concluded that *the vigor of a hybrid was related to the degree of genetic dissimilarity of its parents.* Second, since the morphology of flowers and the breeding systems of plants suggested that nature favored natural crossbreeding, Koelreuter concluded that *hybrid vigor was of particular significance in evolution.* Both of these observations have withstood the test of time and inquiries involving a diversity of living organisms. Each of them is a warning to those who would provide genetic interpretations of heterosis. Since hybrid vigor is both correlated with and the outgrowth of biological evolution, it would be nothing short of folly to expect a single cause for heterosis. Among other things, Koelreuter predicted the potential value of hybrid vigor in forestry, a prediction that has been realized in the rapid development of hybrid forest trees only in the past two decades.

Animal breeders in the early nineteenth century observed that the major value of inbreeding, the fixation of desirable characters, was coupled with the equal danger of inbreeding deterioration. The depression that follows inbreeding was observed also in many plant species. In his characteristically thorough manner, Darwin summarized these experiences, together with his own extensive research on fertilization, in a monumental book, *Cross- and Self-Fertilization in the Vegetable Kingdom,* first published in 1876. Darwin chose plants in preference to animals for these studies because large populations could be grown and both self- and cross-fertilization could be practiced. He concluded that "cross-fertilization is generally beneficial, and self-fertilization injurious," and his comparisons of the vigor of crossed and selfed plants, particularly in corn, sparked an avalanche of plant-breeding research on this subject. By the time of the rediscovery of Mendel's paper, few genetic phenomena had been studied as intensively as inbreeding depression and hybrid vigor.

Commercial use of heterosis

Heterosis often is so striking that statistical tests are not needed to prove its economic significance. The cross of two corn inbreds, for example, commonly produces F_1 hybrids whose seed yields exceed twice those of the parents (see Fig. 5.1). The commercial use of hybrids in the United States now extends to most chickens, corn, tomatoes, onions, and sorghum. It is extending also to an increasing

Fig. 5.1. Hybrid vigor in corn. Representative plants and ears of two inbreds and their F_1 hybrids are shown. Photographs courtesy of J. M. Poehlman; from *Breeding Field Crops* (Holt, 1959); reproduced by permission of Holt, Rinehart and Winston, Inc.

proportion of annual ornamentals and forest trees. The regular, commercial production of hybrids by the controlled mating of selected lines (usually inbred) also occurs in silkworms, sugar beets, poultry, swine, aspen, fir, larch, pine, petunia, marigold, sunflower, zinnia, cabbage, broccoli, cucumber, squash and watermelon, to name a few. Most commercial hybrids are single crosses, made by mating two individuals or inbred lines. In field corn, double cross hybrid seeds, obtained by mating two single cross hybrids, are marketed. Seeds of a single cross hybrid, for example, A × B, must be obtained from the poor ears of a corn inbred (see Fig. 5.1.). In contrast, the seeds of the double cross (A × B) × (C × D) are obtained from the vigorous ears on a hybrid plant. It is much more economical, therefore, to produce and sell double cross seeds.

Most commercial hybrids exceed their parents in performance for certain desired traits. Many, however, do not exceed in yield the varieties from which their own (inbred) parents were derived. It is often the genetic constancy of hybrids that, in addition to their high vigor, makes them more popular than the inconstant varieties from which they were derived. As the parent lines of a hybrid are progressively inbred and become increasingly homozygous, the hybrids become progressively less variable. Theoretically, the cross of two fully homozygous inbreds would produce F_1 plants having no genetic variance at all; why?

Combining ability is an expression of the heterosis of hybrids in which an individual participates. In 1322, in one of the first recorded cases of artificial insemination, an Arabian chieftain is said to have stolen sperm of a neighbor's prized stallion for insemination of his own animals. We may speculate that the stallion had proved himself to have good combining ability. In the United States alone, almost 3,000 bulls of recognized combining ability are used for artificial insemination. The high combining ability of these bulls is expressed in high milk or beef production of their progeny, and it is usually tested extensively before the bulls are used to any great extent. Consider, for example, the magnificent Holstein bull in Fig. 5.2, whose full name is WH-57 Spruceleigh Monogram Rag Apple 1119686 S.M.P. By 1963, at the age of 13, Rag Apple had been used in over 100,000 matings! When Rag Apple's daughters were compared critically with herdmates in milk and butterfat production, the statistics compiled below were obtained.

	Rag Apple's herdmates	Rag Apple's daughters
Annual milk production in lbs.	13,502	14,856
Per cent butterfat	3.59	3.96

Fig. 5.2. A Holstein bull of outstanding combining ability, WH-57 Spruceleigh Monogram Rag Apple. Photograph courtesy of the Western Pennsylvania Artificial Breeding Cooperative, Clarion, Pennsylvania.

Fig. 5.3. Heterosis in an interspecific hybrid of the yak and the domesticated cow. This female hybrid exceeded its larger parent species (cattle) by over 20 per cent in body weight. Photograph from *J. Heredity*, 29 (1938), 31; reproduced by permission of the editors of the *Journal of Heredity*.

These differences in milk and butterfat production may appear small to the uninitiated, but they represent a lucrative expression of high combining ability to the owners of Rag Apple.

The role of genetic diversity in the expression of hybrid vigor, first noted by Koelreuter and emphatically verified by H. K. Hayes and E. M. East 150 years later, is emphasized by the striking vigor of certain diverse hybrids. Few exceptions occur to the principle that hybrid vigor increases in proportion to increasing genetic diversity. Exceptions generally result from its extension to wholly unrelated species. Hybrids like the mule (60-chromosome mare × 66-chromosome ass) illustrate both the heterotic (vigor, size) and depressing (sterility) effects of wide crosses. Hybrids of cattle and species like the yak (Fig. 5.3) also show hybrid vigor (20 per cent above their larger parent) in mature body weight. Although males of this cross are sterile, as are male cattaloes (crosses of cattle and buffalo), females of the same crosses are relatively fertile. The potential value of this combination of hybrid vigor and sterility is illustrated by the tropical fish tilapia. These freshwater fish reproduce so rapidly that overcrowding quickly occurs in farmers' ponds. Tilapia struggle for existence in the overcrowded pond, and gain less than half a pound per year. Certain interstrain hybrids, however, produce sterile males that are vigorous and that grow rapidly. Ponds seeded with these hybrids cannot increase in population, and the heterosis for growth rate is fully expressed in a growth of almost 3 pounds per fish per year. Agricultural uses of hybridization, therefore, relate in many cases to expressions of hybridity in addition to heterosis itself.

Genetic basis for heterosis: Dominance

In the history of the development of scientific concepts and their application for the benefit of mankind, heterosis deserves a prominent position. Probably no two historians would judge the contributions of different people to the origin of the heterosis concept in the same way. Many investigators prior to 1900 had extended Darwin's findings with corn to a wide assortment of plant and animal varieties. Breeders were struck by the necessity of crossbreeding for the maintenance of vigor, recording that inbreeding was "disastrous, an enemy of vigor and yield." Other investigators contributed useful hypotheses over a period of almost three decades that were fitted into the heterosis theory as into a giant jigsaw puzzle.

In 1904, a small experimental garden was established on Long Island which played a prominent role in development of the heterosis concept. In this garden, George H. Shull made successive self- and cross-fertilizations in corn, principally as part of his study of the inheritance of ear-row number. The deteriorating effects of inbreeding at once became apparent to Shull (recall Fig. 2.10). He was particularly impressed, however, by the rejuvenating effects of crossbreeding among the inbreds, and suggested in 1907 that breeding practices should have as a central objective the maintenance of the most vigorous and productive hybrid combinations. Representative of his data are those of the 1910 planting, which included fifth generation inbreds, their F_1 hybrids, and F_2 lines obtained by selfing the F_1 hybrids, summarized below:

	Seed yields (bushels/A.)	Plant height (cm.)
Parent varieties	73.3	265
Inbreds	25.0	193
F_1 hybrids	71.4	257
F_2 populations	42.6	233

Shull suggested that, like W. A. Johannsen's beans (Chapter 1), a field of corn was a heterogeneous mixture of many genotypes. Whereas Johannsen had found that varieties of the self-fertilizing bean were composed of many homozygous genotypes, Shull recognized that varieties of the cross-pollinated corn were composed of many heterozygous genotypes. Inbreeding in corn was, therefore, followed by genetic segregation and by a slow increase in uniformity among inbred lines.

Shull asserted that hybrid vigor was associated inevitably with heterozygosity, and deterioration with homozygosity. The term *heterosis*, proposed to describe the vigor of heterozygous hybrids, supplanted East and Hayes's earlier *heterozygosis*. While the cumulative action of dominant, favorable genes could be held to account for much hybrid vigor, it seemed to both Shull and East that genes must be present in a heterozygous state for the maximum expression of heterosis. Here we find a question no less intriguing and important today than it was a half century ago; is heterozygosity per se necessary for the full expression of heterosis?

Dominant, linked growth factors

The dominance theory of heterosis states that hybrid vigor results from the action and interaction of dominant, often linked growth factors. Heterozygosity is not considered essential to the full expression of heterosis. Theoretically, individuals homozygous for favorable growth factors should be equally as vigorous as individuals heterozygous for the same factors. The importance of linkage to the tenability of this theory was recognized by Donald F. Jones, who first stated the dominance hypothesis in a clear and convincing way in 1918.

A hypothetical dominance model for heterosis is diagrammed at the top of the following page. Parental inbreds are assumed to be homozygous for different alleles at five loci so that the hybrid is heterozygous for all loci.

$$A_0A_0B_1B_1C_0C_0D_1D_1E_0E_0 \times A_1A_1B_0B_0C_1C_1D_0D_0E_1E_1$$

$$A_0A_1B_0B_1C_0C_1D_0D_1E_0E_1$$

In the absence of dominance, the hybrid would be intermediate to its parents. Assuming that alleles with the subscript 1 are dominant, however, the hybrid would be superior to both of its parents. For example, if we allow each recessive genotype (X_0X_0) to contribute one unit and each dominant genotype $(X_0X_1$ or $X_1X_1)$ to contribute two units, the cross above would provide the metrical results below.

$$7 \times 8$$
$$\downarrow$$
$$10$$

An immediate objection to the dominance hypothesis arose as a result of the apparent inability of geneticists to obtain purebreeding lines as vigorous as F_1 hybrids. In terms of the dominance hypothesis, it appeared possible to obtain with comparative ease homozygous inbreds equal in performance to the most heterotic of hybrids. For example, self- or cross-fertilization of the fully heterozygous hybrids described above would segregate an equally vigorous genotype, homozygous for all five dominant alleles, $A_1A_1B_1B_1C_1C_1D_1D_1E_1E_1$. This genotype would be recovered with a frequency of $(\frac{1}{4})^5$, or of 1 in 1,024 F_2 plants. Immediately a purely mathematical problem in obtaining a homozygote with vigor comparable to its heterozygous parent arises from the fact that, as the number of loci (n) governing a metrical trait increases, $(\frac{1}{4})^n$ may become very large indeed. W. Ralph Singleton has estimated that, if $n = 30$ for yield in corn (a reasonable estimate in most breeding lines), it would be necessary to plant a land area 2,000 times that of the earth in order to obtain one F_2 homozygote equal in yield to that of the F_1 hybrid, assuming dominance at all loci.

A second objection to the dominance theory of heterosis was the apparent symmetry of F_2 distributions obtained from F_1 hybrids. The distributions of data for metrical traits showing heterosis were found to be symmetrical, just as for traits in which no dominance occurred. It was emphasized by critics that, with the dominance theory, normal distributions should not be obtained in segregating populations. For example, if dominance at five loci is assumed as in our example above, the six phenotypic classes of an F_2 population occur in the following frequencies.

$$0.1\% + 1.5\% + 8.8\% + 26.4\% + 39.5\% + 23.7\%$$

Asymmetry of this sort was expected to be evident even to the casual observer, yet such asymmetries were not obtained. Several factors militate against the objection that asymmetry would occur in these segregating populations, however. In the first place, asymmetry is reduced considerably by environmental effects, as well as by incomplete dominance and increasing gene numbers. Jones emphasized an additional factor of great importance: linkage. If the dominance theory was true, linkage would tend to reduce the expected asymmetry of segregating populations. Also, the linkage of unfavorable recessive genes with favorable dominant genes affecting the same trait would reduce greatly the frequency with which the multiple dominant chromosomes were recovered.

It is conventional to regard heterosis as any excess in vigor of a hybrid over the midpoint between its parents.

$$\bar{x} \text{ (of } F_1) > \frac{\bar{x}_{P_1} + \bar{x}_{P_2}}{2}$$

We considered in Chapter 4 a scale of values in which dominance was expressed as d, the deviation of a heterozygote from the midpoint between its homozygous parents.

In terms of the dominant growth factor hypothesis, heterosis represents a summation (Σ) of the d values for segregating genes.

$$\text{Heterosis} = \Sigma \, d$$

If some loci are dominant in one direction (for example, toward late maturity) and others are equally dominant in the opposite direction (toward early maturity), a cancelling-out effect may occur in the hybrid and no heterosis may be observed. The absence of heterosis, therefore, does not necessarily imply the absence of dominance at the loci influencing a metrical trait.

The formula Heterosis $= \Sigma d$ must be modified whenever parent inbreds are not entirely homozygous for polygenes controlling the segregating trait. Mathematically, this modification is made by multiplying Σd by y^2. The factor y is the difference in gene frequency between the two inbreds ($y = 1$ or 100 per cent when each parent is homozygous for different alleles at each locus). Heterosis in F_1 thus becomes a summation of the products of d and y^2.

$$\text{Heterosis in } F_1 = \Sigma \, dy^2$$

It may further be calculated that the heterosis in an F_2 population (obtained by random mating or self-fertilization of F_1) is equal to half that of the F_1, since heterozygosity is reduced by 50 per cent in this one generation.

$$\text{Heterosis in } F_2 = \frac{\Sigma \, dy^2}{2}$$

The expected heterosis in other types of progenies (for example, father-daughter matings) can be calculated by reference to their degrees of genetic relationship (see Chapter 2). In practice, the heterosis of F_2 populations closely approximates 50 per cent of the heterosis of F_1 hybrids. This is illustrated in the following plant-height data from tobacco crosses by H. H. Smith.

Inbred parent (P_1)	47.8 inches
Inbred parent (P_2)	28.7 inches
Midpoint between P_1 and P_2	38.3 inches
F_1 hybrid ($P_1 \times P_2$)	43.2 inches
F_2 population	40.6 inches

Although the F_1 hybrid exceeded the parental midpoint by 4.9 inches, the F_2 exceeded it by only 2.3 inches. The variance analysis of heterosis in such an example is made by directly applying the dominance theory discussed in Chapter 4. When the phenotypic variances for the tobacco-height data were analyzed by Smith, the following variances were obtained (V_N could not be calculated).

$$V_G = 180.5 \qquad V_D = 67.3$$
$$V_A = 113.2 \qquad V_E = 25.8$$

In the absence of dominance, V_D equals zero. In the tobacco height example, however, the dominance component contributed almost a third of the total genetic variance. These calculations substantiate the important role of heterosis in tobacco-plant heights. They also provide a base for the estimation of heritability of plant height (55 per cent), and could be used to estimate genetic gains upon selection for this important metrical trait.

Nonallelic interactions and bottlenecks

The dominance theory of heterosis takes into account the potential contribution to hybrid vigor of nonallelic gene interactions. Perhaps the most important type of nonallelic interaction in heterosis is that of complementary genes. If dominant alleles A_1 and B_1 are required for completion of a particular synthetic pathway, the homozygotes $A_0A_0B_1B_1$ and $A_1A_1B_0B_0$ would fail to complete this synthesis. The unique ability of hybrids between these homozygotes to complete the synthesis might be recorded as a form of heteross. The bottleneck concept of nonallelic gene interaction in heterosis was formulated by A. J. Mangelsdorf. This concept states that *the excellence of a genotype, like a chain, depends not upon its strongest link but upon its weakest link,* placing emphasis not only on the superiority of a hybrid but on the inferiority of its parents. This inferiority is conferred by weak links or bottlenecks. A bottleneck refers here to alleles or genotypes that are inadequate in performing the task required of them, so that they act as limiting factors for other gene action.

A naturally occurring example of the bottleneck model of heterosis was provided by W. J. Robbins. Growth rates of excised tomato roots were recorded in culture solutions (Fig. 5.4). Roots of the Red Currant variety were stimulated greatly by the addition of a vitamin, pyridoxin, to culture media. It was concluded that Red Currant had bottleneck loci that limited root elongation by reducing the natural supply of pyridoxin. Roots of the Johannesfeuer variety showed no response to added pyridoxin, but were stimulated by the addition of another vitamin, nicotinamide. Johannesfeuer evidently had bottleneck loci that limited its natural supply of nicotinamide. Roots from hybrids of the two varieties grew more vigorously in all cultures than did roots from the parents. The hybrid was better able to produce both of the vitamins, having the active alleles that overcame bottlenecks in syntheses of the two vitamins. Heterosis, therefore, resulted from the simultaneous occurrence of active alleles from different loci that cooperated to promote root elongation.

Dominance is not implied in a model of heterosis such as this. We need only assume that A_0A_0 is less efficient than A_0A_1 and A_1A_1, and so forth for other alleles. The heterozygotes in a digenic model, $A_0A_1B_0B_1$, appear heterotic in root growth because one parent ($A_0A_0B_1B_1$) has a bottleneck at the A locus while the other parent ($A_1A_1B_0B_0$) has a bottleneck at the B locus. The extent to which nonallelic gene interactions occurring with or without dominance influence the expression of heterosis and inbreeding depression is not known, but their potential significance is very great.

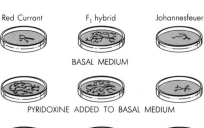

Red Currant　　F₁ hybrid　　Johannesfeuer

BASAL MEDIUM

PYRIDOXINE ADDED TO BASAL MEDIUM

NICOTINAMIDE ADDED TO BASAL MEDIUM

Fig. 5.4. Excised tomato roots grown in sterile culture media provide a possible physiological explanation of heterosis. Roots of the variety Red Currant appeared deficient for pyridoxin, and Johannesfeuer roots appeared deficient for nicotinamide. Roots of the F₁ hybrids, however, elongated well in all media and showed only a slight stimulation upon the addition of either vitamin.

Genetic basis for heterosis: Overdominance

The overdominance theory of heterosis states that heterozygosity per se is necessary for the full expression of heterosis. It is not inferred that dominant, linked growth factors do not contribute to heterosis, rather, the overdominance theory states that they alone cannot account for the entire expression of heterosis. If we consider a given locus A_1/A_0, overdominance may be expressed as the superiority of the heterozygote A_0A_1 over both homozygotes as illustrated by *od* on the scale below.

A_0A_0	Midpoint	A_1A_1	A_0A_1
	←———— *a* ————→	← *od* ————→	

No homozygote can be obtained that equals in performance the over-dominance heterozygote. There are several convincing examples of overdominance involving metrical traits governed by single loci (referred to as one-gene heterosis). Evidence that overdominance contributes measurably to heterosis for polygenic traits, however, is harder to find and much more hotly disputed. The potential importance of an overdominance contribution to heterosis is so great, however, that it is a subject of great interest in quantitative and population genetics. (See Lawrence E. Mettler's *Population Genetics and Evolution* in this series.)

We will consider four types of allelic action leading to one-gene heterosis in heterozygotes that have been suggested as a plausible basis for overdominance. These four types are outlined in the following table for two hypothetical homozygotes, A_0A_0 and A_1A_1, and their hybrid, A_0A_1.

	Products of genotypes		
	A_0A_0	A_1A_1	A_0A_1
Supplementary action	X	Y	$X + Y$
Alternative pathways*	X in E_1	X in E_2	X in E_1 and E_2
Optimal amount	$0.1X$	X	$2X$
Hybrid substance	X	Y	Z

* E = Environment; X, Y, and Z = phenotypes

Supplementary allelic action

When two alleles perform a different function or produce entirely different products (X and Y in the table above), the heterozygote may be able to perform both functions. This, in essence, is supplementary allelic action. It has been illustrated by the clover-leaf-marking alleles in Fig. 3.1 and is perhaps best known for the allelic series governing blood-group antigens and incompatibilities. This type of allelic action in heterosis is illustrated in a particularly interesting way by the alleles governing the resistance of flax to flax rust. H. H. Flor demonstrated that multiple alleles occur at five loci that confer resistance to several hundred strains of the rust. Each allele confers resistance to a different strain, and allelic heterozygotes are resistant to both strains. For example, if flax of the genotype M_1M_1 is resistant to strain 1 and M_2M_2 resistant to strain 2, the heterozygote M_1M_2 will be resistant to both strains. In a natural population attacked by two rust strains such as these, heterozygous M_1M_2 plants alone would survive. In this circumstance, we may properly refer to the heterozygote as heterotic for fitness, and to the supplementary allelic action as an example of overdominance. The effect of such a genetic mechanism on fitness (reproductive potential) might result in a high selective advantage for the allelic heterozygotes in natural populations of flax. This type of heterosis, with its prominent effect on reproductive ability, has been termed euheterosis by Theodosius Dobzhansky, with the connotation that it may not be completely comparable to the heterotic luxuriance of many manmade hybrids. Luxuriance may have no effect, or even an adverse effect, on reproductive ability.

In poultry, a striking demonstration has been made of the association between heterozygosity for blood group factors and heterosis for important economic traits such as hatchability and egg production. Large numbers of alleles occur at the A, B, and other blood-group loci in poultry. Chicks with the highest degree of blood-group heterogeneity (that is, with the largest number of antigens) prove also to have the highest degree of heterosis for economic traits. Among the possible explanations of this association is the occurrence of supplementary allelic action among loci closely linked to the blood group loci. Although the underlying genetic mechanism of these data is disputed, it is not disputed that serological tests pay their way in attaining maximum heterosis in hybrid chicks.

Alternative synthetic pathways

A second type of allelic action proposed as a basis for one-gene heterosis is that of alternative synthetic pathways. This differs from supplementary allelic action primarily in the role that environment assumes. Among the best examples of alternate pathways is that provided by temperature sensitive alleles of animals and plants. Let us suppose that allele R_1 produces red pigment with maximum expression at 80°F.; let us further suppose that allele R_2 produces the same pigment but is most active at 50°F. In the absence of dominance, the heterozygote R_1R_2 has alternative pathways to call upon in synthesizing this pigment, one active in a low temperature range and one active when it is warm.

The alternative pathway hypothesis is presently best supported by analyses of genetic variance for certain metrical traits. Homozygous inbreds and their hybrids theoretically have no genetic variance; their phenotypic variance is entirely environmental. As we noted in Chapter 1, however, it has been found that the environmental variances are much smaller for hybrids than for their inbred parents. A field plot of corn, for example, is subject during growth to many environmental variations, including changes in temperature, fertilizer availability, and moisture and soil conditions. The hybrids react less violently to these changes than do the inbreds. We may postulate then that the hybrid is heterozygous for many alleles governing alternative synthetic pathways. For example, some alleles may function best on cold days, some on warm. The result of this would be that the hybrid performs well on both warm and cold days, and shows less environmental variation than the inbreds. The genotype's ability to buffer against environmental changes is often referred to as developmental homeostasis or canalization, terms equated by some geneticists with the more general term fitness.

Optimal amount concept

The optimal amount concept of overdominance postulates that the homozygote of one allele produces too little of a given substance while the homozygote of another produces too much (or is hypermorphic). The heterozygote of two such alleles is assumed to produce an amount nearer optimal for the organism. This is probably the most common type of one-gene heterosis. It finds most support from cases in which one allele is an amorph. At least twenty-seven of seventy-five lethal amorphs in *Drosophila* confer heterosis (usually in fecundity) on heterozygotes. In most of these instances, the lethal is a probable deletion of an active allele and the three genotypes thus represent

> No active alleles — lethal
> One active allele — heterotic (optimal amount)
> Two active alleles — wild type

Overdominance of the optimal amount type has been implicated for the hooded awn trait studied by G. Ledyard Stebbins in barley. The awn, a long tip on the seed coat, is bent or hooded by a dominant gene K in barley. By means of a series of seven backcrosses, the K allele was transferred into a line differing from the original pure line by this allele. When the KK and kk lines were crossed, seedlings of the two homozygotes fixed carbon dioxide at about the same rate, whereas this important photosynthetic process increased almost 50 per cent in the heterozygote. Similar results were obtained in many corn hybrids. The ultimate proof of the existence of an optimal amount type of one-gene heterosis rests on the elimination of the contributions of genetic background (main problem: closely linked genes) and nonallelic interactions. Some geneticists would suggest that these two contributions can never be excluded entirely. Their exclusion is virtually impossible when we turn to metrical traits governed by many genes.

Hybrid substances

A fourth type of overdominance, still hypothetical, can be designated as the hybrid-substance type. This has been illustrated above by assuming that homozygote A_0A_0 produces substance X, homozygote A_1A_1 produces substance Y, and heterozygote A_0A_1 produces hybrid substance Z. Although several examples of hybrid substances are known, linking them unequivocally with one-gene heterosis is a vexing problem. Hybrid substances were first postulated by M. R. Irwin and L. J. Cole to account for unique antigen components found in the cells of hybrid doves. When doves of the Pearlneck strain were mated with Ring doves, for example, the hybrids could be shown to have nearly all of the antigenic substances of the two parents, plus one or more components not found in either parent. There is evidence that these hybrid substances are not the result of allelic interaction (one-gene heterosis) but of nonallelic gene interactions.

An intriguing example of hybrid enzymes comes from studies of the lactic dehydrogenase enzymes in animal tissues. When the lactic dehydrogenase is extracted from the breast of a six-day-old chick embryo, nearly all of the enzyme is of a form that occurs in the heart tissue of mature birds. This heart dehydrogenase (HD) in the baby chick is gradually replaced during development by a dehydrogenase characteristic of the liver (LD). At the time the egg hatches, a major fraction of the breast enzyme is LD. If one extracts and separates the lactic dehydrogenases from embryos between six days and hatching, however, five distinct enzyme fractions are obtained. Two of these are the pure HD and LD enzymes; the other three act as hybrid enzymes —they can be precipitated by antiserums to both HD and LD.

The lactic dehydrogenase molecule (31,000 molecular weight) was found to be separable into four subunits each about 8,000 in molecular weight. It is proposed that these subunits are of two basic types, H and D. Heart lactic dehydrogenase is thus seen as a natural tetramer of four H units, $HHHH$. Similarly, LD is visualized as a tetramer, LLLL, and it is suggested that the three molecular hybrids in developing chick embryos are $HLLL$, $HHLL$, and $HHHL$. These multiple enzymes of chick muscles may give the developing organism an adaptational or buffering capacity similar in many respects to that which we noted for heterotic hybrids in a varying environment. Although none of these studies of hybrid substances has been proved to involve one-gene heterosis, they offer exciting biochemical examples of hybrid substances that may play a role in the expression of overdominance.

One other approach is made by quantitative geneticists to examine the contribution of overdominance in heterosis. This approach is an extension of the method for estimating dominance discussed in Chapter 4. When dominance is complete, $d/a = 1$. It is suggested that when $d > a$ (that is, when $d/a > 1$), overdominance occurs. Preliminary calculations of this sort indicate a probable contribution of over-dominance to yield in corn. Circumstantial evidence for overdominance has also been obtained from studies of natural populations. Heterozygotes often occur with greater frequencies than can be predicted from frequencies of the respective alleles; this evidence is taken by some investigators to support the superiority of heterozygotes. Plant and animal breeders concur, however, in considering overdominance to be negligible for most metrical traits.

The scientifically inquisitive mind cherishes exceptions to rules. Thus it is at once a joy and frustration to a geneticist to find that few of his laws stand the test of time. The general rule that heterosis does not involve heterozygosity per se is probably as intriguing a target for research as any in genetics. Exceptions to this rule have been suggested in diverse attacks on the problem; only time will assess the validity and importance of these exceptions. Let it suffice to have described some of them, without implying that they make the dominance theory of heterosis untenable; they do not. If anything, the tenuous evidence for overdominance seems to encourage the view that the dominance theory of heterosis is, as biological theories go, an uncommonly reliable one for applied research.

Fixation of heterosis

The asexual reproduction of a hybrid provides one obvious way in which heterosis may be fixed. For example, nearly all of the commercial bananas are from two heterotic triploid hybrids, Gros Michel and Cavendish, that have been reproduced asexually throughout the world. An important form of asexual reproduction in plants is apomixis, the development of seed in the absence of fertilization. Apomictic seeds often develop from maternal diploid cells, making the offspring genetically identical to their mother plant. The genetic constancy of apomictic offspring posed an early puzzle to Mendel, who unknowingly selected the apomictic genus *Hieracium* for studies almost as extensive as those he conducted on peas. When he crossed different species of *Hieracium,* the F_2 and later generations often "agreed fully with their hybrid parents," failing to segregate for any of the traits distinguishing the parent species. Mendel reported (rather sadly, we may conjecture) that the *Hieracium* studies contradicted those of garden peas. The fixation of heterosis by apomixis is common among citrus fruits, blackberries, roses, bluegrasses, and many other flowering plants.

Genetic fixation of heterosis can result from the combination of lethal genes and certain chromosomal rearrangements. Naturally occurring inversions, first discovered by A. H. Sturtevant in *Drosophila,* illustrate this system very clearly. The inversion of a section of chromosome results in a situation like that diagrammed below.

Parent chromosome   *A B   C D E F   G H* . . .
Chromosome with inversion *A B   F E D C   G H* . . .

In an individual heterozygous for an inversion, crossovers occurring within the inverted region lead to sterile gametes. Since crossovers within the inverted region fail to survive, inversions are said to be crossover suppressors. Let us suppose that a mutation of *C* to c^1 occurs on the parent chromosome, with the c^1 allele acting as a lethal when homozygous.

Mutant parent chromosome   *A B c^1 D E F   G H* . . .

Let us further suppose a similar mutation of *D* to the recessive lethal allele d^1 on the inverted chromosome.

Mutant inverted chromosome   *A B   F E d^1 C   G H* . . .

We now have the necessary ingredients for the fixation of heterosis. Of the three possible combinations of these mutant chromosomes, only the following heterozygote will survive.

$$\frac{A\ B \quad c^1 D\ E\ F \quad G\ H\ \ldots}{A\ B \quad F\ E\ d^1\ C \quad G\ H\ \ldots}$$

Since crossovers within the inverted region are suppressed by the sterility of crossover gametes, heterozygosity for the inverted region is perpetuated. This type of balanced lethality is most prevalent among hymenopteran insects (bees, wasps, etc.), in which the males are haploid, and in *Drosophila,* in which crossing over does not occur in the male. It does not occur commonly in other insects, or in other animals and plants.

A more prominent role in the fixation of heterosis is probably played by translocation, an example of which can be found in the lowly cockroach. No one who has lived with or near cockroaches doubts their extraordinary adaptability and apparent hybrid vigor. When the first sailing vessels touched the shores of the new world, the common

"American" cockroach *Periplanata americana* appears to have wasted no time getting on board, for it is now found throughout the world. The American cockroach is commonly heterozygous for one or more translocations (see Fig. 5.5), which appear in meiotic metaphase as enlarged rings of four chromosomes. Designating any two chromosome pairs as $1 \cdot 2$ and $3 \cdot 4$ and the corresponding translocated chromosomes as $1 \cdot 3$ and $2 \cdot 4$, a translocation ring like those in Fig. 5.5 might be represented as

$$
\begin{array}{c}
1{\cdot}2 \text{\textemdash} 2{\cdot}4 \\
\mid \qquad \mid \\
1{\cdot}3 \text{\textemdash} 3{\cdot}4
\end{array}
$$

Gametes from this heterozygote will survive only if they include a complete set of chromosome arms, and therefore they must be $1 \cdot 2 + 3 \cdot 4$ or $1 \cdot 3 + 2 \cdot 4$. Other combinations are genetically deficient and usually lethal to gametes. Recombinations of the two surviving gamete types would produce

$\frac{1}{4}$ homozygous $\frac{1}{2}$ heterozygous $\frac{1}{4}$ homozygous

$$
\frac{1 \cdot 2}{1 \cdot 2} + \frac{3 \cdot 4}{3 \cdot 4}
\qquad
\begin{array}{c}
1{\cdot}2 \text{\textemdash} 2{\cdot}4 \\
\mid \qquad \mid \\
1{\cdot}3 \text{\textemdash} 3{\cdot}4
\end{array}
\qquad
\frac{1 \cdot 3}{1 \cdot 3} + \frac{2 \cdot 4}{2 \cdot 4}
$$

If we were now to assume, as we did in the case of inversions, that a recessive lethal mutation, l_1, occurs on the $1 \cdot 2$ chromosome, the homozygous class to the left above would not be recovered. Similarly, the

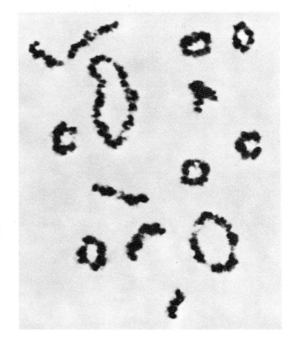

Fig. 5.5. Meiotic chromosome preparations from the cockroach *Periplaneta americana* reveal two naturally occuring translocation complexes (the enlarged rings of four chromosomes) in addition to the twelve normal chromosome pairs. Photograph courtesy of B. John.

appearance of a recessive lethal, l_2, on the $2 \cdot 4$ chromosome would lead to lethality of the corresponding homozygotes. The heterozygote above would then be a balanced lethal, heterozygous for both recessive alleles, l_1 and l_2, and only its heterozygous progeny would survive.

Heterozygosity may thus be fixed or enforced by the combination of translocations and recessive lethal genes. Translocation heterozygotes may also be kept at a high frequency in populations (as in the cockroach, perhaps) when the associated genes are not lethal but only subvital or slightly deleterious to the homozygotes. Translocation rings are common among natural populations, not only of cockroaches but of snails and many flowering plants. In many species of the evening primrose, *Oenothera*, genetic segregation is almost completely suppressed by a balanced lethal system and an intriguing complex of translocations.

The fixation of heterosis may also occur as the result of polyploidy. The vigor of a species cross like that between wheat and rye is observed not only in the diploid hybrids, which are sterile, but also in amphiploid hybrids in which the chromosomes have been doubled. The doubled species hybrids often are fully fertile, and their offspring continue to show the heterosis arising from the combination of genes from the two parent species. Almost half of our cultivated plants are of amphiploid origin, and it is to the subject of polyploidy that we now turn.

References

Gowen, J. W., *Heterosis*. Ames: Iowa State University Press, 1952. A classic compilation of papers reviewing all aspects of this subject.

Lerner, I. M., *Genetic Homeostasis*. Edinburgh: Oliver and Boyd, Ltd., 1954. For a thorough study of overdominance, see this.

Mather, Kenneth, "The Genetical Basis of Heterosis," *Proc. Roy. Soc.* (*London*), *Ser. B.*, *144* (1955), 143-50. The problem of nonallelic interaction is considered in detail; compare with Lerner's *Genetic Homeostasis*.

Swanson, Carl P., *Cytology and Cytogenetics*. Englewood Cliffs, N.J.: Prentice-Hall, Inc., 1957. See Chapter 15 for a discussion of balanced lethals.

Problems

5.1. Referring to the corn yields from Shull's 1910 planting, calculate expected yields and heights for F_2 and F_3 populations.

5.2. The best method of predicting the yield of the double cross hybrid, $(A \times B) \times (C \times D)$, is to average the yields of the 4 single crosses, $A \times C$, $B \times C$, $A \times D$, and $B \times D$. Why? Which 2 of these 6 possible single crosses would you mate to obtain maximum heterosis when A and D are sister inbreds and B and C are also sister lines?

5.3. Assigning 5 units to alleles with subscript 0, and 10 units to alleles with subscript 1, calculate metrical values for parents and F_1 hybrids of the cross, $A_0A_0B_1B_1C_1C_1 \times A_1A_1B_0B_0C_0C_0$, when (a) no dominance occurs, (b) when A_1 is dominant to A_0, and (c) when A_1 is dominant to A_0 and B_1 is dominant to B_0.

5.4. Derive and graph the following F_2 frequency distributions for the 3 models assumed in Problem 5.3.

Metrical value	(a)	(b)	(c)
30	$\frac{1}{64}$	$\frac{1}{64}$	$\frac{1}{64}$
35	$\frac{6}{64}$	$\frac{4}{64}$	$\frac{2}{64}$
40	$\frac{15}{64}$	$\frac{9}{64}$	$\frac{7}{64}$
45	$\frac{20}{64}$	$\frac{16}{64}$	$\frac{12}{64}$
50	$\frac{15}{64}$	$\frac{19}{64}$	$\frac{15}{64}$
55	$\frac{6}{64}$	$\frac{12}{64}$	$\frac{18}{64}$
60	$\frac{1}{64}$	$\frac{3}{64}$	$\frac{9}{64}$

Six

Polyploidy

Polyploidy refers collectively to all natural and induced variations in chromosome number. Variations arise in the numbers of genomes (chromosome sets), in the numbers of individual chromosomes in a genome, and in the numbers of segments of individual chromosomes. These differences are commonplace among related species. For example, seedless table bananas regularly have thirty-three chromosomes, while the seedy "monkey bananas" (only monkeys eat them) have twenty-two chromosomes. Differences also occur commonly within species, as we have noted with regard to the honeybee, whose queen and worker females have thirty-two chromosomes, yet whose males have but sixteen. Similarly, differences arise between cells within an individual. For example, mice infected with the Ehrlich ascites cancer have eighty chromosomes in most cancer cells but only forty in non-malignant body cells. Polyploidy, although relatively insignificant in animals, has been of major importance in the evolution and breeding of plants. This fact remains something of a biological puzzle, although, as we shall see, it is probable that sex is involved.

Occurrence of polyploidy

The evolution of higher plants owes much to the increase of chromosome numbers accompanying poly-

90

ploidy, since it is widespread among mosses, ferns, and flowering plants. Nearly half of the important cultivated plants are polyploids; most of these are euploids (tetraploids, hexaploids, etc.) that have even multiples of the basic chromosome set. New polyploids created by geneticists and breeders have assumed increasing agricultural importance. At least a hundred "tetra" or "triploid" varieties of flowering plants appeared in American seed catalogs alone in the 1950's. Apart from the giant sequoia and a few other species, however, polyploids are not common among the gymnosperms and woody flowering trees. Polyploidy is more common in perennials than in annuals, in alpine than in lowland plants, and in plants that reproduce asexually than in those that reproduce sexually.

In contrast to plants, none of the commercially important animals is wholly polyploid, although sporadic polyploid cells and tissues may be found in all animals. Tissue cultures of mammalian cells often increase in chromosome number, however; the classic *HeLa* strains of human cells, for example, stabilized around mean chromosome numbers ranging from the triploid to subtetraploid levels. It was suggested by H. J. Muller as early as 1925 that sex might account for the inability of polyploid animals to survive the battle of natural selection. Studies of sex determination (see Chapter 2) revealed that polyploidy upset the often delicate balance of sex-determining genes, causing intersexuality and sterility. Two predictions that stem from this theory have encountered difficulty in proof. One is that hermaphroditic animals, lacking sex chromosomes, should be expected to be polyploid as often as are hermaphroditic plants. The other is that dioecious plants, which have sex chromosomes, should not be polyploid more often than are vertebrate animals. Experimental evidence supports neither of these predictions, for hermaphroditic animals are rarely polyploid (and those few largely parthenogenetic). At the same time, dioecious plants with sex chromosomes are often polyploid (strawberries, yams, willows). It is apparent, however, that polyploidy has a more severe effect on sexual balance in animals, with their long evolutionary history of sex-chromosome differentiation, than it does on sex in plants, where sex chromosomes are relatively recent developments.

Among the effects of polyploidy, four are of special significance in agriculture. (1) Any change in chromosome number changes genetic segregations accordingly. (2) Any increase in chromosome number provides a mask or cover for deleterious recessive genes. Polyploids often lose entire chromosomes or chromatin segments without phenotypic effect, because of the presence of other chromosomes carrying the same genes. As a result, the genetic load of deleterious mutations can increase greatly in a polyploid. (3) Chromosome increase is accompanied almost inevitably by larger cell size (Fig. 6.1), hence the superior agricultural performance of many polyploids. (4) Gamete sterility and lowered fecundity often accompany polyploidy.

Polyploid animals include an odd assortment of sow bugs, sawflies, flatworms, leeches, brine shrimp, roundworms, and so on, most of which reproduce parthenogenetically (without fertilization). Similarly, polyploidy is almost universal among apomictic (parthenogenetic) plants such as blackberries, bluegrasses, and dandelions. Asexually reproducing yeasts, tissue cultures, tumors, and galls also include large numbers of polyploid cells. These facts suggest that asexual reproduction circumvents the major disadvantages of polyploidy, of which sterility is probably first in importance.

Endopolyploidy and polyteny

Endopolyploidy—the presence of polyploid cells in otherwise diploid tissues—arises when nuclear divisions occur without cell division. Endopolyploidy was first noted among spinach root cells that show chromosome numbers ranging upward from $2n = 12$ (diploid) to $2n = 96$ (16-ploid). Later, endopolyploidy was found in animal tissues. Mid-gut cells of mosquitoes, for example, show chromosome numbers ranging from $2n = 6$ (diploid) up to $2n = 96$ (32-ploid). Ovarian tumors in *Drosophila* develop highly polyploid eggs, and in another insect, *Gerris*, the giant salivary gland cells may have chromosome numbers exceeding 2,000-ploid! Polyploidy is characteristic of the root nodules formed in response to infection by nitrogen-fixing bacteria, and is common among the "giant cells" in nematode-induced galls. It is probable that such infections do not induce polyploidy, but rather they create a cellular environment in which the polyploid cell thrives.

The duplication of genetic material may take place without chromatid separation, producing an association of chromatids in bundles known as polyteny. The classic example of polytene chromosomes is that first observed in the *Drosophila* salivary cell in 1881. These giant polytene chromosomes appear to burst at times of physiological activity, producing the so-called Balbiani rings. At these times, individual chromatids stretch or despiralize, expanding to form puffs along the chromosome. Estimates of the number of chromatids in the polytene bundle range as high as 16,000 in the beetle *Chironomus*. Polyteny is more common in metabolically active tissues such as ovarian nurse cells and gut epithelia, an association that is our best clue to its possible significance.

It has been increasingly evident that the chromosomes of higher plants and animals have a form of endopolyploidy at the molecular level. Light microscope studies prior to 1940 revealed that the ana-

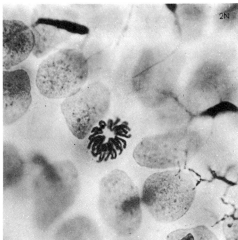

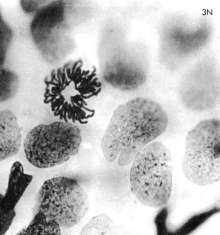

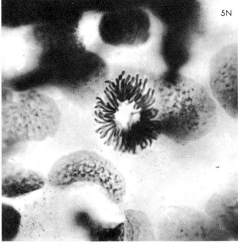

Fig. 6.1. Cells in the tailtips of diploid, triploid, and pentaploid salamanders. Photographs courtesy of G. Fankhauser.

phase chromatid consisted of two closely paired half chromatids. By 1948 B. P. Kaufmann reported substantial evidence for four microscopically visible strands at this stage. Electron micrographs supported this evidence and suggested even further subdivision of the chromosome into microfibrils of about 120 Å (.000012 mm.) in diameter. The DNA double helix is known to be about 20 Å in diameter. It is evident that two DNA helixes could make up the characteristic 120 Å microfibril. In turn, between 8 and 100 microfibrils could be accommodated on the basis of volume into the chromatid at anaphase, which has a diameter of about 1,000 Å. It can be estimated in this manner that the chromosome might consist of between 16 and 200 DNA molecules, probably paired closely somewhat like the strands of a Manila rope.

Chromosome fragmentation leads to a form of apparent polyploidy in animals such as the nematode *Ascaris*. Chromosome numbers in somatic tissues of this worm range from $2n = 52$ up to $2n = 72$, greatly exceeding those of cells in the germ line $(2n = 2)$. The distinction between germ-line and somatic cells occurs at the first division of the *Ascaris* zygote, and fragmentation occurs only in the somatic line. Irradiation induces fragmentation similar to that of *Ascaris* in plants such as the wood rush *Luzula*, in which centromere activity is diffused throughout the chromosomes. Fragments that are acentric (lacking centromeres) cannot divide and are soon lost in most plant and animal tissues. Each fragment in *Ascaris* or *Luzula*, however, acts as though it possessed a functional centromere. The fragmentation in *Ascaris* is referred to as apparent polyploidy, since no actual gene duplication is involved. The genetic or physiological basis for fragmentation is, to say the least, obscure. One interesting result of centromere diffusion is that these nematodes and woodrushes are extremely resistant to death by irradiation!

Types of polyploids

Euploids are polyploids that differ from the basic diploid number $(2n)$ by entire genomes or chromosome sets; common examples of euploids are

Monoploids ("haploids")	n	Tetraploids	$4n$
Triploids	$3n$	Hexaploids	$6n$

Aneuploids are polyploids which differ from the basic diploid number by one or a few chromosomes; the following are common types.

Nullisomics	$2n - 2$	Trisomics	$2n + 1$
Monosomics	$2n - 1$	Tetrasomics	$2n + 2$

Euploids may be classified further according to the origin of the added chromosomes or genomes; autopolyploids result from direct genomic increase within a species, while allopolyploids contain two or more genomes from different species or genera.

Polyploids have been among the most rewarding tools in cytogenetic research since R. R. Gates discovered in 1909 that Hugo de Vries's startling mutation, gigas, in *Oenothera* was a natural tetraploid. The gigas mutant well deserved its name, having large and thickened flowers and leaves. Plant breeders did not effectively exploit this gigantic aspect of polyploidy, however, until the discovery in 1937 of the alkaloid colchicine in the autumn crocus. Colchicine has the still perplexing effect of arresting spindle activity and anaphase chromosome separation in animal and plant cells, as well as the equally perplexing effect of curing gout. Leaving chromosomes suspended at metaphase, colchicine treatment doubles the chromosome number of a cell. It has been used successfully to induce polyploids in many hundreds of plant species and a few animals. Other agents, such as nitrous oxide and heat shocks, also have been used to induce polyploidy, but few so successfully as colchicine. Isolated cases of polyploid-inducing genes are known. In *Drosophila*, the gene lethal-polyploid inhibits anaphase separation periodically and causes much endopolyploidy (usually lethal). Polyploid tissues also arise in undifferentiated scar tissue near grafts and wounds. In what way is this observation consistent with cytological studies of tissue cultures and insect galls?

Autopolyploids

Autopolyploids such as de Vries's gigas arise by direct increase in the number of genomes. Prolonged treatment with colchicine, for example, can create numerical series of $4n$, $8n$, $16n$, and so on; hybridization among these types leads to intermediate euploids of $3n$, $5n$, and so on. Almost startling arrays of polyploidy appear in plants such as *Saccharum spontaneum*, a species of wild sugar cane distributed from Africa to Japan. Different wild forms of *S. spontaneum* have somatic counts of 40, 48, 64, 80, 96, and 128, along with many intermediate numbers. In most species there appears to be an optimum level of polyploidy above which added chromosomes or genomes lead to depression of growth and vigor. In the ferns and grasses, for example, this optimum level of ploidy may be very high indeed, as it is for the vigorous bluegrass *Poa litorosa*, which is 38-ploid (see Fig. 6.2).

Monoploids (known also as haploids) are readily distinguished by their weakness and sterility. In bees, wasps, and ants, the males are derived from unfertilized eggs and are monoploid (see Chapter 2). The failure of chromosome pairing at meiosis causes monoploids to be wholly sterile in most species. However, the monoploid honeybee males produce functional sperm by virtually circumventing the meiotic pairing process. While monoploids do not survive at all in most animals,

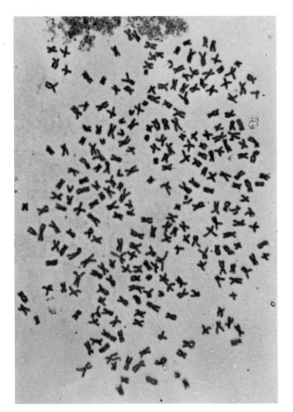

Fig. 6.2. Somatic division showing 265 chromosomes in the 38-ploid *Poa litorosa*. Photograph courtesy of J. B. Hair.

those induced in axolotls and salamanders by Gerhard Fankhauser (recall Fig. 6.1) developed slowly but surprisingly well. Like plant monoploids, they were fully sterile. While monoploids occur in most plants as rare mutants, certain lines of corn produce more than 30 monoploids per 1,000 plants. There is evidence of a polygenic system controlling this high rate of monoploidy.

Doubled monoploids may occur as spontaneous sectors on monoploids, or they may be induced by colchicine and other agents. They represent probably the only fully homozygous genotypes available in higher organisms. Doubled monoploids have been studied in detail in tomato, cotton, corn, and other crops with an eye to the potential value of these as ready made, homozygous inbred lines. Among 10,000 inbred seedlings of a doubled monoploid in tomato, a self-pollinated plant, W. S. Lindstrom could find only three plants in any way distinct from the original parent, and no significant variations were observed in nine later generations. On the other hand, an equally extensive series of doubled monoploids studied by G. F. Sprague in corn, a cross-pollinated plant, showed quite different behavior. A diverse assortment of characters segregated in the inbred generations from doubled monoploids of corn, including both monogenic and polygenic traits. The basis for this genetic variation is unknown.

Autotetraploids result from the doubling of diploids and have been induced in nearly all the agriculturally significant genera of plants. The doubled cells are regularly larger, resulting in the larger size of certain tissues and organs (see Fig. 6.1). This is evident especially in the stomates, pollen grains, seeds, and flowers. Partial fertility and slow rates of genetic segregation reduce the commercial value of many induced autotetraploids. Increased flower size, however, has made autotetraploidy important to the ornamental breeder, and increased fruit size has made it equally interesting to fruit breeders (see Fig. 6.3). Comparatively few natural autopolyploids are agriculturally important species. Among these are the autotetraploid potato, coffee, peanut, alfalfa, and orchard grass, and the autohexaploid sweet potato, plum, and timothy. Autotriploids rarely produce functional sex cells, and the resulting sterility accounts for the economically valuable seedlessness of triploid bananas, limes, and seedless watermelons (see Fig. 6.4), to cite a few. In other triploid species, such as azaleas and lilies, sterility insures long flower life and consistent annual bearing. Triploid salamanders, also sterile, have larger cells in some tissues than the diploid (see Fig. 6.1). Since other tissues develop less rapidly, however, the over-all effect of triploidy on salamander body size is not noticeable. In contrast, triploid aspens are commercially successful giants, growing more rapidly and luxuriantly than either diploids or tetraploids. Triploid sugar beet hybrids are being developed by crossing cytoplasmically male-sterile diploids with tetraploid lines. Triploid offspring such as these combine the advantages of both hybrid vigor and polyploid vigor.

Fig. 6.3. Increase in fruit size of the Perlette grape following colchicine-induced tetraploidy. Photograph courtesy of Haig Dermen.

Fig. 6.4. Cross section of seedless triploid watermelon, showing a few of the rare collapsed seeds. To the right, sterile pollen grains from the triploid plant. Photographs courtesy of O. J. Eigsti.

Allopolyploids

Allopolyploids are euploids containing at least two distinct genomes. Often these arise upon the doubling of chromosomes in a species hybrid, producing an amphidiploid or double diploid hybrid. A classical series of allopolyploids makes up Nagahara U's triangle in the cabbage family (see Fig. 6.5). Cabbage, mustard, and turnip make up the corners of this interesting triangle. Cytological studies of these *Brassica* species revealed a series of related chromosome numbers, 8, 9, and 10. In addition, three species with gametic numbers 17, 18, and 19 acted as connecting links to the corners of U's triangle. Ojvind Winge proposed in 1917 that the higher numbers of this series were natural polyploids that might have arisen following hybridization of the corner species, with subsequent genome doubling. For example,

$$AA \times BB \rightarrow AB$$
$$AB + AB \rightarrow AABB$$

Winge's hypothesis of the amphidiploid origin of these and other plants has been more than amply verified by the genetic reconstruction of such important crops as tobacco and cotton through the doubling of chromosomes in species hybrids.

Doubled hybrids have at once two major advantages. First, they contrive to capture the hybrid state itself, with whatever heterosis or unusual hybrid features two diverse genomes create. *Raphanobrassica*, for example, is the amphidiploid hybrid of radish and cabbage. Plant breeders who achieved this difficult cross probably hoped for a plant with the root of a radish and head of a cabbage. As luck would have it, of course, the hybrid combined the root of a cabbage with the leaves of a radish. Hybrids such as those studied extensively by Arne Muntzing between rye and wheat (*Triticale*), however, show more promising combinations of the valuable traits of the two parents.

A second major advantage of doubled hybrids is the high fertility commonly distinguishing them from the undoubled hybrids. The high gamete and seed fertility of amphidiploids reflects the regularity of meiosis in these hybrids, a regularity also reflected in the diploid nature of gene segregations. Diploid segregations and meiotic regularity both arise from the tendency of chromosomes in the amphidiploid to pair preferentially in bivalents (intragenomic pairing), rather than in the multivalents found in autotetraploids.

Allotetraploids may be produced by crossing the autotetraploids of two different species. Further intercrosses and backcrosses lead to mixtures of allo- and autopolyploidy that have been dubbed segmental allopolyploidy by G. Ledyard Stebbins. In exhaustive studies of polyploids, Stebbins concluded that most natural polyploids were segmental allopolyploids, possessing a large number of homologous chromosomes and chromosome segments but still differing to such an extent that the undoubled hybrids are sterile.

Creating what has become the most extensive assortment of homemade polyploids, breeders of orchids currently synthesize and select segmental allopolyploids at a rapid pace. The discovery in the 1950's that flower size and conformity in orchids was enhanced by polyploidy accounts for this burst of activity. In the orchid genus *Vanda*, for example, the showy variety "Nellie Morley" was found in 1955 to be a triploid species hybrid with fifty-seven chromosomes. Many other large-flowered hybrids soon were shown to be polyploid. The orchid can produce as many as a million seeds in each flower, so that even

Fig. 6.5. U's triangle of diploid and amphidiploid species of *Brassica*.

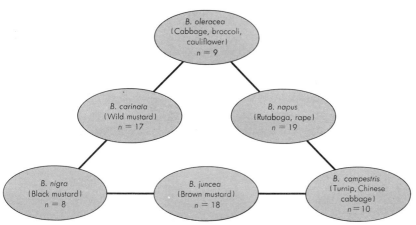

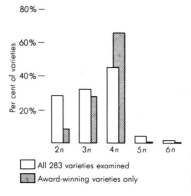

Fig. 6.6. Polyploidy among commercial Hawaiian orchids. Wild parent species are all diploid (2n). Based on experiments of Haruyuki Kamemoto.

triploid and pentaploid hybrids produce occasional fertile seeds. These polyploid hybrids, now being produced with gay abandon by amateur breeders, bring home the prize money (see Fig. 6.6), as if to confirm again Darwin's statement that hard cash is a good criterion of genetic superiority.

Aneuploids

The discovery in the 1950's that aneuploidy leads to idiocy, sterility, and sexual aberrations in man came as little surprise to plant geneticists. Many of de Vries's outstanding offtypes in the evening primrose, obtained about the time of the rediscovery of Mendel, were later shown to be aneuploids. It is the rare diploid species that remains unaffected by the loss or addition of a chromosome.

Monosomics are diploids that lack a single chromosome $(2n - 1)$. Aneuploids of this type do not survive at all in most animals and plants. This is true even of species such as corn and tomato, in which monoploids (lacking an entire genome) are not at all uncommon. The fact that the loss of an entire genome is less damaging than the loss of a single chromosome stresses the importance of homeostasis or genetic balance within the genotype of a living organism. Why might the study of monosomics from doubled monoploids be of interest in this connection? Monosomics are found with comparative ease among high polyploids. In the allotetraploid tobacco and allohexaploid wheat, strains monosomic for nearly all chromosomes have been isolated. These monosomic lines, although subnormal, survive and even reproduce fairly satisfactorily. Although few of the monosomic male gametes $(n - 1)$ are viable, monosomic eggs survive about half as well as the euploid eggs. It is evident that loss of genetic material is of less consequence to a highly polyploid species than it is to diploids.

Nullisomics $(2n - 2)$ have been obtained by the self-pollination of monosomics in several plants. The nullisomic plant lacks both homologues of any given chromosome. Monosomics and nullisomics have both been used in the location and transfer of genes. A new mutant gene in wheat, for example, may be located with comparative ease by crossing it with all twenty-one nullisomics and studying the segregating generations from these crosses.

Trisomics $(2n + 1)$ occur sporadically in many diploid organisms, and may be obtained easily from crosses of diploids and triploids. For example, trisomics make up almost 30 per cent of the progeny when triploid petunias are crossed with pollen from diploid plants. An added chromosome almost always causes partial sterility of pollen and seeds. This accounts in part for variations in fruit shape and size recorded by A. F. Blakeslee in his classic studies of the genus *Datura*. The shapes of burs or spiny fruits in *Datura* differed so greatly in the twelve different trisomics that they could be used to distinguish each with ease. In many other plants, trisomics do not differ so obviously from each other, particularly when fruit morphology cannot be used. In general, the phenotypic effect of an added chromosome is more pronounced in commercial, highly bred species than it is in wild forms. It is apparent also that added chromosomes have more serious consequences in animals than in plants.[1] This appears to be due to the wide distribution among animal chromosomes of genes with important embryological effects.

Aneuploids of almost all types occur in other plant genera. Apomictic polyploids such as garlic, blackberries, and bluegrasses include almost every conceivable chromosome number, from diploid up to octoploid and higher. The ability of these plants to reproduce without fertilization makes meiotic difficulties and sterility of little or no consequence to them. As chromosome numbers increase in an aneuploid series, added individual chromosomes have less effect on phenotype. Animals like the bedbug and flatworm and plants like onions and rye often are aneuploids, carrying small extra chromosomes which do not pair with those of the basic genome. These accessory or B chromosomes are generally smaller in size and appear genetically inert. It is interesting to recall our observation that the chicken has six major pairs of chromosomes, together with about sixty-six microchromosomes (see Fig. 2.2). Since genes have been located in only six linkage groups in poultry, this would suggest that the sixty-six microchromosomes are genetically inert. In this sense, they may be comparable to the accessory chromosomes of bedbugs or of onions.

----

[1] See, for example, the discussion of human trisomics in Victor A. McKusick's companion text in this series, *Human Genetics*.

Genetic segregations in polyploids

Genetic segregations in polyploids differ from those in diploids in three important respects. First, an increase in chromosome number permits a corresponding increase in the number of different alleles at any locus. Second, meiotic segregations in a polyploid often lead to sterile gametes, affecting genetic ratios accordingly. Finally, the meiotic segregations in a polyploid, unlike those of the diploid, depend on the linkage relationship between gene and centromere, and on the frequency with which chromosomes associate in multivalent complexes.

In the case of multiple allelic loci, polyploidy presents the opportunity for increased genetic information in the polyploid cell. The following terms have been applied by S. S. Atwood to the genotypes involving a single, multiple allelic locus in a tetraploid.

Monoallelic	$S_1S_1S_1S_1$,	$S_2S_2S_2S_2$, etc.
Diallelic	$S_1S_1S_1S_2$,	$S_1S_1S_2S_2$, etc.
Triallelic	$S_1S_2S_3S_3$,	$S_1S_1S_2S_3$, etc.
Tetra-allelic	$S_1S_2S_3S_4$,	$S_2S_3S_4S_5$, etc.

Tetra-allelic and other multiallelic types can occur only in polyploid cells, and may confer new genetic potentialities on the polyploid. When alleles such as those of the M, L, and P loci, which confer rust resistance on flax plants, govern resistance to individual races of a pathogen, the tetraploid may be resistant to a great number of races. In the case of multiple allelic systems that govern antigen, blood-group, or incompatibility systems, polyploidy similarly offers the organism increased biochemical complexity. The increased genetic carrying capacity of a polyploid has been studied in only a few systems, such as that of self-incompatibility in flowering plants, where it is evident that multiallelic types become the most prevalent class in natural populations.

A tetraploid produces diploid gametes that may be heterozygous or homozygous for any given locus. The tetra-allelic tetraploid $S_1S_2S_3S_4$ produces six types of heterozygous gametes in equal proportions—S_1S_2, S_1S_3, S_1S_4, S_2S_3, S_2S_4, and S_3S_4. It has been shown, however, that homozygous gametes—S_1S_1, S_2S_2, S_3S_3, and S_4S_4—are also produced by the tetra-allelic genotype. In white clover, for example, about 8 per cent of the gametes produced by plants tetra-allelic for the S (incompatibility) locus are homozygotes. The discovery that crossing over occurs between chromatids at a stage when chromosomes are effectively double underlies our interpretation of results such as those with white clover. Genes located near the centromere segregate in a different way than do genes located at a great distance from the centromere. Homozygous gametes cannot arise from a tetra-allelic plant if the locus is linked completely with the centromere. If the locus is some distance from the centromere, however, such gametes do occur.

Homozygous gametes from the tetraploid $S_1S_2S_3S_4$ arise in two steps —the production of multivalent configurations by the four related chromosomes, and the occurrence of crossing over between the locus and the centromere. The production of homozygous gametes by this process is a special case, referred to as double reduction, of the unique segregations of polyploids. Depending on the degree of multivalent pairing and crossing over between gene and centromere, we find not one but an entire spectrum of gametic ratios from a polyploid, for which the extreme values alone are easily calculated:

| | Gametic ratios of $AA:Aa:aa$ | |
Tetraploid genotype	*Chromosome assortment*	*Chromatid assortment*
aaaa	0:0:1	0: 0: 1
Aaaa	0:3:3	1:12:15
AAaa	1:4:1	6:16: 6
AAAa	3:3:0	15:12: 1
AAAA	1:0:0	1: 0: 0

One set of extreme values, referred to as chromosome assortment, arises when multivalent pairing does not occur or when crossing over between gene and centromere does not occur. The other extreme, referred to as chromatid assortment, requires maximum crossing over between gene and centromere, and 100 per cent multivalent formation. The ratios above may be calculated most easily by assuming 4 segregating units (chromosomes) in the case of chromosome assortment, and by assuming 8 segregating units (chromatids) in the case of chromatid assortment. These ratios all presuppose the occurrence of random pairing among the four chromosomes involving the locus under study. Whenever preferential or intragenomic pairing occurs (as in many amphidiploids) the segregations are entirely different. For example, the genotype $A_1A_1A_2A_2$ could produce only A_1A_2 gametes if the four chromosomes paired preferentially, A_1 with A_1 and A_2 with A_2.

A single pair of alleles acting without dominance can be combined to give five different phenotypes in tetraploids. Multiple allelism increases this phenotypic variation astronomically. For the metrical character in which five diallelic loci are involved, segregation of $5^5 = 3,025$ phenotypes is possible in the tetraploid versus $3^5 = 243$ in the diploid. The search for a particular genotype (for example, one homozygous for all five genes) thus becomes an impressive if not impossible task in the tetraploid. This is reflected in the practices of plant breeders who deal with polyploids; sugar cane breeders in Hawaii, for example, attribute much of their genetic advance with this polyploid grass to the procedure of screening almost ten millon seedlings in segregating families each year.

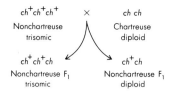

$ch^+ch^+ch^+$ × $ch\ ch$

Nonchartreuse   Chartreuse
trisomic   diploid

ch^+ch^+ch ch^+ch

Nonchartreuse F_1 Nonchartreuse F_1
trisomic   diploid

Segregations of F_2 plants (from trisomic F_1 selfed):
(a) Observed: 9 diploid, chartreuse
             82 diploid, nonchartreuse
             26 trisomic, nonchartreuse
             0 trisomic, chartreuse

(b) Expected genotypes:

Female gametes	Male gametes ($n + 1$ are nonfunctional)	
	$\frac{1}{3}ch$	$\frac{2}{3}ch^+$
n gametes $\begin{cases}\frac{1}{6}ch \\ \frac{2}{6}ch^+\end{cases}$	$\frac{1}{18}ch\ ch$ $\frac{2}{18}ch^+ch$	$\frac{2}{18}ch^+ch$ $\frac{4}{18}ch^+ch^+$
$n + 1$ gametes $\begin{cases}\frac{1}{6}ch^+ch^+ \\ \frac{2}{6}ch^+ch\end{cases}$	$\frac{1}{18}ch^+ch^+ch$ $\frac{2}{18}ch^+ch\ ch$	$\frac{2}{18}ch^+ch^+ch^+$ $\frac{4}{18}ch^+ch^+ch$

(c) Expected F_2 phenotypes:
$\frac{1}{18}$ diploid, chartreuse
$\frac{8}{18}$ diploid, nonchartreuse
$\frac{9}{18}$ trisomic, nonchartreuse
0 trisomic, chartreuse

Fig. 6.7. Genetic segregations for chartreuse (ch), recessive mutant in tomato, following crosses with plants trisomic for chromosome 8. Based on experiments of C. M. Rick.

Altered segregations in polyploids may be used to localize genes to certain chromosomes. Trisomic, monosomic, and nullisomic lines have been synthesized in several important cultigens largely for this purpose. For example, all possible trisomics have been produced in tomato, corn, and *Datura*, and all monosomics have been produced in wheat and tobacco. Studies of chartreuse, a greenish-flowered mutant in tomato, serve to illustrate the use of trisomics for gene location (see Fig. 6.7). Chartreuse was shown initially to be inherited as a single recessive gene, ch. Crosses then were made of the chartreuse diploid to twelve nonchartreuse plants, each trisomic for a different one of tomato's twelve chromosomes. In all but one of the twelve F_2 families, chartreuse and nonchartreuse segregated in a 1:3 ratio. The one aberrant ratio identified chartreuse as a gene located on chromosome 8. Male gametes carrying an extra chromosome 8 do not function in the tomato, and female gametes carrying this trisome function poorly, as indicated in Fig. 6.7 by the low recovery of trisomic F_2 plants (versus 50 per cent expected).

Gene juggling

The transfer of genes to commercially important organisms from related wild species has been increasingly profitable in plant and animal improvement. Monogenic traits of high economic value (for example, disease resistance) have an exasperating way of turning up in useless, weedy relatives of cultigens. As a consequence, breeders have incorporated liberal genetic contributions from weedy relatives to varieties of sugar beets, tobacco, wheat, sugar cane, and strawberries, to cite a few examples. Polyploidy has opened up some of the most profitable avenues for this type of gene juggling.

Few areas of research are so inherently intriguing as that of trying genes out in a new genome or species. If we were able to transfer one gene at a time from one species to another, as the bacterial geneticist occasionally does with his transducing viruses, most animal- and plant-breeding problems might quickly be solved. Three interrelated types of gene juggling will be considered: chromosome engineering, gene transfer, and genome reconstruction.

Chromosome engineering in tobacco

Early attempts failed to locate resistance to tobacco mosaic virus (TMV) in commercial tobacco, *Nicotiana tabacum.* A wild diploid relative, *N. glutinosa* (genome formula GG) was known to be entirely resistant to TMV. The resistance was based on a single dominant gene. Unfortunately, *N. glutinosa* crossed only poorly with the allotetraploid *N. tabacum* (genome formula $T^1T^1T^2T^2$), forming sterile triploid hybrids (GT^1T^2). Chromosome-doubled hybrids of this cross $(GGT^1T^1T^2T^2)$ were produced by R. E. Clausen and T. H. Goodspeed. These hybrids were fully fertile and true-breeding amphidiploids, and were dubbed "*N. digluta.*" Preferential chromosome pairing occurred intragenomically (G with G, etc.) in "*N. digluta.*" As a result, crossing over between the *glutinosa* and *tabacum* genomes failed to occur. It appeared to be impossible, therefore, to transfer the dominant TMV-resistant gene to the *tabacum* genome by crossing over.

Surprisingly enough, however, F. O. Holmes was able to select tobacco plants fully resistant to TMV following several backcrosses of "*N. digluta*" to *N. tabacum.* Selfing and further selection resulted in the "Holmes Samsoun" TMV-resistant variety. By crossing it to monosomic lines of tobacco, Holmes Samsoun was shown by Dan Gerstel to have twenty-three pairs of *tabacum* chromosomes plus one pair (chromosome H) from *glutinosa,* carrying the TMV-resistance gene. This H chromosome had simply replaced one in the *tabacum* genome. Although mosaic-resistant, the Holmes Samsoun variety showed several undesirable features such as reduced leaf size due to the presence of other *glutinosa* genes on the substituted H chromosome. Lines having direct substitution of chromosomes from alien species rarely satisfy the breeder's objectives since entire chromosomes commonly include genes that are altogether undesirable. Thus the transfer of small gene blocks, or preferably of single desirable loci, has been of increasing interest to the chromosome engineer.

Gene transfer in wheat

Gene transfer can occur in either of two ways—between homologous chromosomes by crossing over, or between nonhomologous chromosomes by translocation. Both methods have been used successfully in gene juggling, resulting in the transfer of relatively small gene blocks to cultigens. In one of the most carefully detailed gene juggling studies, E. R. Sears transferred little more than a single gene for leaf-rust resistance to common bread wheat from the wild grass *Aegilops umbellulata*. Common bread wheat, *Triticum aestivum*, is a hexaploid with a somatic number of 42, containing six 7-chromosome genomes (genome formula = *AABBDD*). The weedy *A. umbellulata* is a diploid, $2n = 14$ (genome formula = *CC*). Although crosses of these two species fail, bridging the two are several wheat species that will cross with both wheat and *A. umbellulata*. Sears chose to use the tetraploid emmer wheat *T. dicoccoides* (genome formula = *AABB*), crossing it to *Aegilops* (*CC*) to produce sterile triploid hybrids (*ABC*). These were colchicine doubled, giving fertile 42-chromosome amphiploids (*AABBCC*), which were partially cross-fertile with bread wheat.

The F_1 hybrids (*AABBCD*) between wheat (*AABBDD*) and the emmer–*Aegilops* amphiploid (*AABBCC*) produced fourteen bivalents (*AA* and *BB*) and fourteen unpaired chromosomes (*C* and *D* genomes). These hybrids were grassy in appearance, resistant to rust and highly pollen sterile although they did produce some seeds when crossed. Repeated backcrosses were made of these hybrids to bread wheat, and rust-resistant plants were constantly selected. Among these, many proved to be trisomics with forty-three chromosomes, having a single C chromosome added. Apart from their poor fertility, the trisomics carried too many undesirable *Aegilops* characters, such as earliness of flowering and low seed production, to be of any direct use.

Sears accomplished the final coup by irradiating the 43-chromosome plants prior to meiosis and applying pollen taken from the irradiated plants to the pistils of normal wheat plants. Among the 6,091 progeny were 132 rust-resistant plants. Twelve of these were shown to have reciprocal chromosomal interchanges. Each of these could be assumed to have had a section of the *Aegilops* chromosome containing the rust-resistant gene transferred to a wheat chromosome. Most of the translocation heterozygotes were partially sterile, and showed other *Aegilops* characters, indicating that relatively large chromosome segments had been involved in the translocations. Among these translocations, however, one plant was rust resistant and showed no grassy characters.

Cytological study revealed that it had a minute translocation involving little more of the *Aegilops* chromosome than the gene for resistance. This plant was fully fertile, and produced the desired leaf rust–resistant source for the breeding work. Gene transfer by translocation or crossing over rarely if ever involves only the single gene locus desired. Breaking linkages is thus one of the most constant and discomforting problems of gene transfer faced by the breeder.

Genome reconstruction

The origin of the genomic furniture of many plants is known quite precisely. This is seldom the case for animals. Polyploid plant species like cotton, plums, raspberries, strawberries, and sorghum are a few that, like wheat and tobacco, have been synthesized entirely or in large part from their diploid relatives. Genome reconstruction, involving the addition or replacement of entire genomes, has been applied to these and other polyploid species in studies of evolutionary patterns and as an aid to gene juggling.

Newly synthesized amphidiploids provide valuable information about the evolutionary history of polyploids. In addition, they often set the stage for more profitable gene juggling, as illustrated by studies of the cultivated American cotton *Gossypium hirsutum*. This cotton species is an allotetraploid having two genomes, A from an Asian species and D from an American species. Crosses of American cotton $(AADD)$ with the African diploid *G. anomalum* produce sterile triploid hybrids. S. G. Stephens produced triploids of this type that carried dominant marker genes from *G. anomalum*. When the triploids were doubled to form the allohexaploid hybrid, little or no genetic segregation occurred for the dominant markers chosen. This was interpreted to mean that *G. anomalum* has a genome (designated B) that is largely nonhomologous with the A or D genomes. This theory was confirmed by the low frequency of multivalent formation in the $AABBDD$ hybrids. Even the rare interchanges of genes between *anomalum*'s B genome and the A and D genomes of cultivated cotton, however, make probable the future use of *G. anomalum* as a source of genes for cotton improvement.

References

Burnham, C. R., *Discussions in Cytogenetics*. Minneapolis: Burgess Publishing Co., 1962. A particularly thorough exploration of the cytogenetics of polyploids may be found in Chapters 6, 7, 8, and 9.

Muntzing, Arne, *Genetic Research*. Stockholm: LTs Förlag, 1961. Many examples of polyploids and polyploid hybrids are detailed in Chapters 24 and 25.

Swanson, Carl P., *Cytology and Cytogenetics*. Englewood Cliffs, N.J.: Prentice-Hall, Inc., 1957. See especially Swanson's discussions of endopolyploidy and endomitosis in Chapter 9.

Problems

6.1. The white color of flowers in white clover is based on duplicate, dominant, nonlinked genes, R_1 and R_2; red-flowered plants are homozygous $r_1r_1r_2r_2$. What are the expected ratios of red- and white-flowered plants in the F_2 from a cross of homozygous red- and homozygous white-flowered tetraploids assuming (a) chromatid, and (b) chromosome inheritance?

6.2. In the exhaustive studies by A. F. Blakeslee and O. S. Avery of aneuploids in the genus *Datura*, trisomics comprised 29, 22, and 10 per cent of the self-pollinated offspring of trisomic types Globe, Glossy, and Elongate, respectively. The trisomics did not transmit through the pollen. What would be the expected F_2 ratios for each of these trisomics in tests similar to that diagrammed in Fig. 6.7?

6.3. The chromosome in wheat on which a new recessive mutant occurs may be ascertained by observing F_1 hybrids of the homozygous mutant with all 21 nullisomics. What crosses would you make to determine the chromosome on which a new dominant mutant is located?

6.4. Chromosome pairing at meiosis in monoploids of the 48-chromosome potato, a tetraploid, is considered to reflect an autopolyploid origin of the species. Why? The numbers of chromosome pairs at meiosis in monoploids of the potato and 4 other species are given below, with somatic numbers and numbers of genomes (e.g., 4X, 6X, etc.).

Number of pairs	Species	Somatic number
12	*Solanum tuberosum* (potato)	48 (= 4X)
12	*Solanum nigrum*	72 (= 6X)
8	*Medicago sativa* (alfalfa)	32 (= 4X)
7	*Digitalis mertonensis*	112 (= 16X)
1	*Nicotiana tabacum* (tobacco)	48 (= 4X)

Suggest genomic formulas for these monoploids.

6.5. Monoploids derived from 42-chromosome bread wheat (6X) average 1.6 chromosome pairs at meiosis. Monoploids from plants nullisomic for chromosome 5, however, commonly show as many as 7 pairs. Suggest corresponding genomic formulas and a genetic basis for this difference.

Mutation

The birth of a grotesquely dwarfed calf or colt calls our attention in a dramatic way to apparent hereditary errors. The appearance of a new race of disease or of a white sector on a red rose may be less dramatic, but it is of equal interest to the biologist. To sudden heritable changes such as these, Hugo de Vries gave the name *mutation*.

The most prominent of de Vries's mutations was a giant evening primrose named gigas. Later recognized to be a tetraploid sport, gigas aroused a flush of enthusiasm for mutation in the first decade of this century. It is unlikely that many biologists then imagined the extent to which mutation research would grow, or the contributions that it would make, in fifty years. The mutant gene or chromosome is the ultimate source of all genetic variation, serving as the basic molding clay for the onward march of evolution and for genetic advance through selection. In view of the scope of mutation studies, it is perhaps surprising to find that mutation continues to present some of the most challenging enigmas for genetic exploration.

Sudden heritable changes

Given a continuous irradiation of 300 roentgens a day, a chrysanthemum grows into a grotesque caricature of a plant, its leaves and flowers variously colored, spotted, and ir-regular in shape. Once removed from the irradiation, certain of these effects disappear. Others are transmitted to tissues that develop after removal from irradiation, and may be considered permanent changes. Most changes affect patches of somatic tissue from which no germ cells are destined to arise. Somatic mutations commonly occur without affecting easily visible characters. The somatic mutation in pigment synthesis shown in Fig. 7.1, for example, would have no visible effect on leaf cells, root cells, or other plant tissues.

The most important permanent changes induced by irradiation are those transmitted to cells that undergo meiosis. Many of these changes act as gametic or embryonic lethals. The experimental proof that a change is heritable (i.e., that it is a mutation) rests on the very small but important group of changes transmitted through sperm and egg to the offspring. In practice, we designate most somatic changes as muta-tions, since there is often sound basis for the inference that they are heritable.

Fig. 7.1. Somatic mutation affecting petal color in snapdragon. Photograph courtesy of A. H. Sparrow.

Sudden heritable changes also occur without apparent external cause. These spontaneous mutations or sports have been selected carefully by breeders of tulips, mums, and fruit trees, for example, for several centuries. Platinum mink, seedless oranges, and Ancon (shortlegged) sheep are among the spontaneous mutations of recognized value in agriculture. We may find color sports as well as ever-sporting or mutable plants in almost any flower garden, and students of seventeenth century painting should know them well. The cytologist observes naturally occurring chromosome breaks in about two of each thousand cells of a lily root or a human tissue culture, of which many must lead to somatic mutations.

Almost as soon as de Vries had defined mutations as sudden heritable changes, questions arose about the definition and use of this new term. As we shall see, de Vries's own mutations would not fit the definition of mutation preferred by many geneticists today. As luck would have it, de Vries had chosen an extraordinary genus of flowering plants, *Oenothera,* for his most intensive research. Most species of *Oenothera* have sets of chromosomal translocations (see Chapter 5), with a combination of self-incompatibility and lethal genes that makes even the most complex heterozygote behave like a pure line. *Oenothera Lamarckiana,* de Vries's primary test species, was a relatively true-breeding hybrid of the genomes gaudens and velans. The two genomes are homologous only to a limited extent, permitting pairing only at the chromosome ends, with the formation of large chromosome rings at meiosis. Exceptional crossovers occur, however, between nonhomologous parts of the two genomes. These crossovers result in rare genetic recombinants that were recorded as gene mutations; common among them were the nanella dwarfs. Among other conspicuous variants studied by de Vries were tetraploid and trisomic segregants (Chapter 6).

Mutations can be described as rare events, commonly recessive to wild type, often with associated deleterious or lethal effects, and capable of induction by irradiation and a variety of mutagens. The rarity of spontaneous mutations reflects the remarkable precision with which chromosomes divide and separate to daughter cells (see Fig. 7.2). Only in the presence of mutagens, or of certain mutator genotypes, do the frequencies of sudden heritable changes become easily measurable in most organisms. The fact that a character appears rarely in a population (e.g., Mongolism in man) is at best a poor indicator of mutation. Polygenic systems, linkage, gene interactions, and polyploidy all reduce greatly the rates of phenotypic segregation.

An example of rare recombination among linked genes that mimics mutation has been provided in the classical studies of the *R* locus in corn by L. J. Stadler. The *R* gene acts both in endosperm and in plant tissues to produce deep red anthocyanin. When pollen grains from a

Mutations per billion cells	Trait and locus
500,000*	Plant color in corn (R locus)
80,000*	Self-incompatibility in petunia
40,000*	White eye in *Drosophila*
30,000*	Hemophilia in man
10,000*	Chromosome II lethals in *Drosophila*
7,000*	Seven monogenic traits in mice
1,200*	Endosperm maturation in corn (Sh locus)
1,000*	Streptomycin sensitivity in *Chlamydomonas*
2,000*	Histidine requirement in *E. coli* (his^+ to his^-)
40	Histidine requirement in *E. coli* (his^- to his^+)
80	Inositol requirement in *Neurospora* ($inos^-$ to $inos^+$)
7.1	T1 phage resistance in *E. coli* ($T1^s$ to $T1^r$)
1.6	Streptomycin sensitivity in *E. coli* (S^s to S^r)

*Probable causes for these high rates are extragenic, and include deletion, duplication, and recombination.

Fig. 7.2 Some spontaneous mutation rates.

homozygous dominant R^rR^r stock are applied to silks of the colorless rr stock, the triploid endosperms have the genotype R^rrr and are colored. The mutation from colored to colorless seeds was so frequent relative to other genes studied by Stadler (Fig. 7.2) that it aroused suspicion of a unique mutationlike mechanism. In a brilliant series of studies, Stadler and his co-workers showed this to be true. Four of the most common forms of the R locus (referred to as alleles) had been known from the early studies of R. A. Emerson; these were

R^r colored seed, colored plant
R^g colored seed, colorless plant
r^r colorless seed, colored plant
r^g colorless seed, colorless plant

Detailed study of the mutation patterns among these forms indicated that loss of plant or seed color alone were common, while the simultaneous loss of both was exceedingly rare (see Fig. 7.3). Reverse- or backmutations leading to the acquisition of color were not obtained.

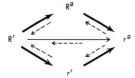

Fig. 7.3. Sudden heritable changes affecting the R locus in corn. Size of arrow indicates relative frequency of changes in that direction; broken lines indicate changes that were not obtained.

Using a series of closely linked marker genes, it was possible to confirm Stadler's early suggestion that the R locus is composed of two tightly linked genes or pseudoalleles. One of these affects plant color (P/p), the other affects seed color (S/s), and the four forms are thus interpreted as $R^r = PS$, $R^g = pS$, $r^r = Ps$, and $r^g = ps$. These two pseudoalleles are sufficiently homologus that, on occasion, they pair. Crossing over at the time of such oblique pairing is known as unequal crossing over. In the R^rR^r homozygote, unequal crossing over led to sudden heritable changes:

$$P \quad S$$
$$\cdots\!\!\times\!\!\underline{\qquad}$$
$$\underline{\quad\cdots}$$
$$P \quad S$$
$$\rightarrow \quad \frac{P\ P\ S}{\cdots} \quad \text{and} \quad \frac{S}{\qquad}$$

$$P \quad S$$
$$\cdots\!\!\times\!\!\underline{\qquad}$$
$$\underline{\quad\cdots}$$
$$P \qquad S$$
$$\rightarrow \quad \frac{P\ S\ S}{\cdots} \quad \text{and} \quad \frac{P}{\qquad}$$

The deficiency crossover gametes P and S showed loss of seed or plant color and were scored as mutations. They arose at the low frequency of about 250 out of a million sperm, and could be distinguished from the nondeficiency types Ps and pS only by detailed linkage studies. The duplication gametes PPS and PSS could not be distinguished from normal PS (R^r allele) gametes. In the R locus studies, an additional class of mutants occurred with a frequency of about 250 per million sperm, and these were not associated with crossing over. Careful linkage studies proved most of the latter mutants to result from minute deletions.

Closely linked pseudoallelic loci are common also in *Drosophila* and perhaps in most organisms. Unequal crossing over in the bar or white eye loci of *Drosophila*, for example, leads to apparent mutants in high frequencies (Fig. 7.2) similar to those noted by Stadler for corn. It will be evident that the difficulty of establishing the origin of a mutation can be very great, even with characters like the colors of corn seeds or *Drosophila* eyes, for which populations of 100,000 individuals can be scored with comparative ease.

Extragenic mutations

Chlorophyll deficiencies and embryo lethals are the most common mutations observed in multicellular plants and animals. The photosynthetic activity of plants and the embryological development of animals present us with systems of particular importance and biochemical intricacy. Many genes play vital roles in each process. The loss or malfunction of any vital gene can lead to dramatic and easily recorded effects. Historically, mutation theory was based on obvious heritable changes of this nature. A very high proportion of these changes have been shown to involve alterations external to the gene itself.

In theory, it is preferable to restrict the definition of mutation to "those sudden heritable changes that alter the activity but not the position of the individual gene." In practice, however, this class of intragenic mutations can be distinguished only with difficulty (if at all) from changes involving blocks of genes, or extragenic mutations. In addition, intragenic mutations are either exceedingly rare or exceedingly difficult to recover in higher organisms.

There are 3 prominent types of extragenic mutations: (1) chromosomal aberrations that involve loss or altered positions of genes—the most important class of extragenic mutations; (2) changes in chromosome number; (3) alterations of modifying or suppressor genes. Changes in chromosome structure and number outyield other types of spontaneous and induced mutations. Presented with a dose of castor oil, a deficiency of calcium ion, or a treatment with gamma rays, the chromosomes of an onion root are broken up readily into many small fragments. Such an astounding variety of chemicals and environmental agents have a similar effect that we may properly marvel at the natural constancy of chromosomes. Nonetheless, chromosomes also break spontaneously in about one out of every 500 dividing cells, or in one out of every 5,000 chromosomes. In seeds, sperm, or pollen grains that have been stored or aged, these frequencies increase greatly.

Breaks may occur in the undivided chromosome or in one or both of the chromatids of the chromosome after DNA replication. Breaks commonly are distributed at random along the length of the chromosome. In over 90 per cent of the cases, the broken ends of a chromosome reunite or restitute in their original state. Most broken chromosome ends fuse within at most a few minutes of breakage. It appears that a broken end that fails to fuse in this time may form an inert end unable to participate in further unions. The ends (telomeres) of chromosomes are similarly inert, and rarely participate in fusion with broken ends. In quite another manner, densely ionizing mutagens such as alpha particles damage the chromosome in such a way that about a third of the broken ends can no longer undergo fusion. The fusion of broken chromosomes requires energy (in the form of ATP, or adenosine triphosphate), oxygen, and protein synthesis. It is a dynamic process and can be influenced greatly by the environment of the cell at the time of breakage.

A single break cuts the chromosome into centric (centromere-containing) and acentric parts. The acentric fragments are commonly lost at subsequent divisions, leaving the cell deficient for the genes on the fragment. Duplications may arise when centric fragments pass by mistake to certain daughter cells. The centric fragments carrying S (incompatibility) alleles have been shown to account for most of the rare self-fertile mutations in plants (see Fig. 7.2). About one of every four spontaneous breaks is an isochromatid break, affecting paired chromatids in nearly the same location. Following the application of ionizing radiation, over three out of every four breaks are of this type.

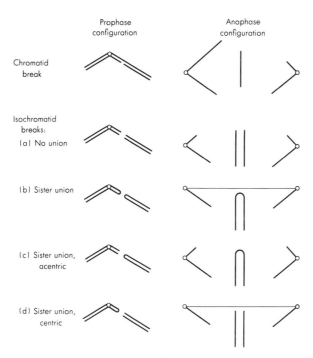

	Prophase configuration	Anaphase configuration

Chromatid break

Isochromatid breaks:
(a) No union

(b) Sister union

(c) Sister union, acentric

(d) Sister union, centric

Fig. 7.4. Some cytological consequences of breakage and reunion among chromatids.

Fusion of the broken chromatid ends in isochromatid breaks occurs in most cells, often linking the separating centromeres together (Fig. 7.4) to produce a chromosome bridge at the following anaphase. Each of the events diagrammed leads to the occurrence of acentric fragments and deletions. Large deletions (for example, any that are cytologically visible) almost always have associated deleterious effects, especially to the sensitive haploid gametes. That deficiencies or deletions comprise the majority of induced mutations helps to account for the popular impression that mutations are harmful. Lethal factors are largely if not exclusively deletions (see Chapter 3), but minute deletions, which probably comprise the majority of visible mutations following treatment with irradiation, need not be lethal and, indeed, may have no ill side-effects whatever.

Fusions of broken chromosomes or chromatids can lead to a diverse assortment of chromosome aberrations, including translocations, inversions, duplications, ring chromosomes, and complex aberrations. Translocations are the most common aberrations in natural populations. A high proportion of translocations involves simultaneous deletion. In addition to the phenotypic effects of the deletion, the translocation of a gene into a new chromosomal location may also have a phenotypic or "position" effect. Position effects are common in *Drosophila* and bacteria, where functionally allied genes are often juxtaposed along a chromosome. The meiotic pairing in translocation heterozygotes leads to the gamete sterility that readily identifies many translocation mutants in higher plants. Even in the mold *Aspergillus,* careful studies of altered linkage relationships revealed that most sublethal mutants were found to include translocations.

Inversions of gene blocks are common following chromosome breakage (recall "Fixation of heterosis" in Chapter 5). Crossing over in inversion heterozygotes leads to gamete sterility, and altered linkages as well as position effects help identify these as extragenic mutations. Most inversions and translocations do not lead to phenotypic change, and may be unrecorded where the chromosomes and gamete sterility cannot be studied easily. Polyploids occur as sporadic mutants in plant cells and are common also in cell and tissue cultures (see Chapter 6). Most common among these are the additions or deletions of single chromosomes, changes with immediate phenotypic effect in nearly all organisms, including man.

Intragenic mutations

The increasing precision of cytological, linkage, and biochemical techniques has permitted us a much clearer view of the gene and the way it can mutate.[1] Mutation research, especially with microorganisms, has helped clarify our definition of the gene. A gene locus occupies a defined length of the chromosome; the gene's information is coded in the DNA molecules of the chromosome. Each gene controls a chemical reaction or class of reactions. Deletion of the entire gene locus commonly results in (1) loss of function, (2) inability of a mutant to revert to wild type, (3) alteration of the linkage of neighboring genes, and often (4) impaired growth of the organism. In microorganisms, at least, such losses or deletions of gene loci usually can be distinguished satisfactorily from intragenic changes.

Within the gene, smaller units known as sites can be identified by crossover-type experiments. A single site is taken as the smallest unit of genetic material that is indivisible by recombination but at which mutation can occur. Intragenic mutations may be single- or multisite in nature. Multisite mutants commonly share many of the features of minute deletions or duplications, and are generally interpreted in this way. Single-site mutations within a gene have been studied in particular detail in the typhoid and colon bacteria and in bacteriophages. Almost 400 sites have been recognized in the *rII* locus of bacteriophage T4 by Seymour Benzer. In these and similar studies, the conclusion appears justified that a single mutational site constitutes a single or, at most, a few nucleotide pairs of the DNA

---

[1] For your further study of the gene as the mutable unit of heredity, consult Franklin Stahl's *The Mechanics of Inheritance* and Philip Hartman and Sigmund Suskind's *Gene Action,* also in this series.

molecule. Although mutations commonly occur at random among the sites, certain sites are referred to as hot spots because mutation occurs there with particular ease.

Bridging the gap from the single-site mutations of virus DNA to the mutations observed in multicellular organisms presents some staggering challenges. In the multicellular organism, DNA is intimately associated with protein and RNA in chromosomes, and is confined by a nuclear membrane throughout most of its existence. The interphase nucleus of mammalian liver cells, for example, incorporates RNA, DNA, histone proteins, and nonhistone proteins in a ratio of 1:9:11:79. DNA contents of these nuclei range up to a million times that of phage DNA. The protein and other nuclear constituents may play important but almost completely unknown roles in mutation.

Another potential level of complexity of the gene as a mutable unit has emerged from studies indicating that the chromosome may exist in most cells as a multiple-stranded bundle of DNA molecules (Chapter 6). It follows that intragenic change in a single DNA molecule of a multiple-stranded chromosome may be like mixing a pinch of salt in a sugar bowl; its phenotypic effect may be negligible. Only if such biochemical changes affected all or most neighboring DNA molecules, or monopolized the molecules as a function of time, could an intragenic change in a single DNA molecule ultimately produce a phenotypic change.

Induction of mutations

Many agents have the ability to break the chromosome, alter the chemical makeup of DNA, or otherwise induce heritable changes. These mutagenic agents are common constituents of our environment and that of the cultigens we grow. Mutagens commonly have the capacity of inducing cell death, either immediately or through a delayed or mitotic death effective at the time of cell division (i.e., as if through dominant lethal mutation). Reversing this observation, we find that many cell poisons are mutagenic; these include cancer-inhibiting agents, herbicides, fungicides, bacteriocides, antimetabolites, and insecticides in common use. Although it is dangerous to generalize, it is apparent that the chromosome and gene may be physiologically or chemically altered by most agents with biological toxicity that can penetrate to the chromosome in sufficient concentration without first killing the cell.

Ionizing radiations

Best known among mutagens are the radiations like X rays that are able to cause ionization in a cell. Each ionization event involves the discharge of an electron from one atom and its corresponding capture by another atom, an event requiring the relatively large, localized energy of thirty-four electron volts. These pairs of ionized atoms are physically unstable and violently reactive. One ionization event is sufficient to inactivate a dry molecule of DNA or of an enzyme. The immediate effect of ionizing radiations appears to be principally the scission (breakage) or cross linking (fusion) of long-chain molecules like DNA.

Soon after Roentgen made his historic discovery of the X ray in 1895, it was shown convincingly that these rays could cause biological damage, such as skinburn (a common early method of estimating dose rate). X rays also were effective in sterilizing spores and seeds, and in the production of widespread abnormalities in living plants or animals. They are equally well known to us today for their ability to cure or induce cancer and to induce mutations of value in agriculture. The radiation arsenal now includes alpha particles, beta rays (electrons), and gamma rays (a form of X ray), available from radioactive isotopes produced in nuclear reactors. In addition, neutrons, protons, and deuterons are available from reactors or generators for biological research. Each of these radiations has proved highly mutagenic to all living systems on which it has been tested.

Radiation dosages are commonly expressed in roentgens (r). The following data indicate some biological effects of differing X-ray doses; they may be compared, for example, with the lifetime gonadal dose (70 yrs.) of man = $10r$ (largely from natural radiations):

1 r	Induces 1 deletion/1,000 cells in human leucocytes
35 r	Doubles the mutation rate of most genes
700 r	Lethal to man
10,000 r	Lethal to a potato
150,000 r	Lethal to a cabbage seed
2,500,000 r	Lethal to all living organisms

The quantitative relationships of dose and response vary for different mutational events. Dose-response patterns are essentially linear (that is, mutation rates increase in direct proportion to dose) for intragenic changes, minute deletions, and breaks involving the chromosome or unpaired chromatids (Fig. 7.5). While the events that occur between ionization and permanent lesion are imperfectly understood, the linearity of dose responses suggests that when a certain number of ionizations occur within a certain critical volume, a mutation occurs. This quantitative relationship gave rise to the target theory.[2] Applied

---

[2] Commended to your attention for further reading is a classic work in the field of radiation biology by D. E. Lea, *Actions of Radiation on Living Cells,* 2nd ed. (Cambridge, 1955).

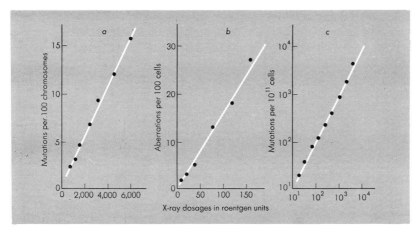

Fig. 7.5. Linear dose response of mutational events following X-irradiation. (a) X chromosome lethals in *Drosophila* (averages of several investigators); (b) isochromatid breaks in *Tradescantia* anthers (based on data of Karl Sax); (c) methionineless backmutations in *Escherichia coli*, plotted for convenience on a log-log scale (based on data of Milislav Demerec and Joan Sams.

to mutations, the target theory assumes the gene to be the target, and mutation to be the result of a "hit" in the gene by a number of ionizations sufficient to alter it. For example, D. E. Lea has calculated that a minimum of 20 ionizations is necessary within a target volume to break the chromosome. Alteration of a target is dependent only on the number of ionizations and not on the time in which they occur, i.e., mutation rates should be independent of the rate at which a dose is delivered. Mutations which increase linearly with dose normally conform to this expectation. If the target theory is true, any radiation dose, no matter how small, should result in an increase of mutation frequency; i.e., there should be no threshold dose below which ionizations are insufficient for mutation to occur. This expectation has been realized for all events that exhibit linear dose response.

The dose responses for certain types of mutational events following irradiation are not linear (see Fig. 7.6). The production of gross deletions (those that can be recorded visually) requires two breaks in the same chromatid. Similarly, translocations require the production of two independent breaks. The induction of these two independent events is nearly proportional to the square of the dose, and the dose response accordingly is nonlinear. In most experiments, however, the dose response of these two-hit events is proportional to $(dose)^{3/2}$. The reduction from the expected $(dose)^2$ appears to result from the restitution of many breaks.

In contrast to these results with X-irradiation, densely ionizing irradiations such as neutrons and alpha particles produce deletions and

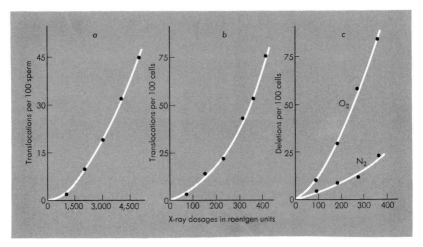

Fig. 7.6. Nonlinear dose response of mutational events following X-irradiation. (a) Translocations in *Drosophila* derived from irradiated sperm (based on data of H. Bauer); (b) translocations in *Tradescantia* anthers (based on data of Karl Sax); (c) interstitial deletions in *Tradescantia* anthers treated in oxygen and in nitrogen (based on data of N. H. Giles and H. P. Riley).

exchanges in direct proportion to dose. The results indicate that with these radiations the two breaks involved are not produced independently but may result from the passage through tissue of a single ionizing particle. This also implies that only those breaks that are close together can participate in an exchange; estimates of this critical distance range from 1 to $\frac{1}{10}$ micron. Dominant lethal mutation rates most nearly mimic gross deletions or translocations in their proportionality to (dose)$^{3/2}$ for X rays, and to (dose)^1 for neutrons.

The earliest evidence for induced mutations appeared before 1920 in studies of fruit flies and Jimson weeds. In 1927, H. J. Muller published a classic paper entitled "The Artificial Transmutation of the Gene"[3] that proved beyond doubt that X-ray treatments increased mutation rates significantly in fruit flies. Concurrent studies of barley by L. J. Stadler confirmed and extended these conclusions. Muller's research with induced mutations is notable if only for the elegant cytogenetic stocks that he devised. Recognizing that mutations were extremely infrequent, Muller first established genetic stocks in which mutations could be recognized with particular ease. The initial technique involved an X chromosome (*ClB*) so marked that lethal mutations resulted in the absence of the male sex among F_2 progeny.

Muller devised an improved method for detecting mutations in the X chromosome using females homozygous for a marked X chromosome

[3] Reprinted in J. A. Peters, ed., *Classic Papers in Genetics* (Prentice-Hall, 1959), pp. 104-16.

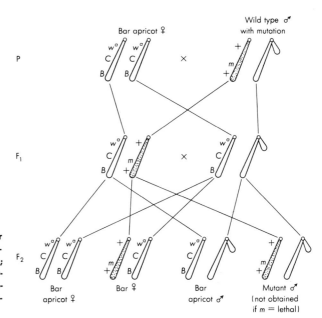

Fig. 7.7. The Muller-5 method for detecting mutations in the X chromosome of Drosophila. B = bar eye; w^a = apricot eye; C = crossover-suppressing inversions; m = proposed mutation, induced or spontaneous.

(see Fig. 7.7). The X chromosome carried two inversions (abbreviated C, for crossover suppressor) that effectively prevented crossing over along the entire length of the chromosome. Males that have been treated with a mutagen are mated to the Muller-5 females, and the F_1 flies are allowed to mate at random. In the F_2 progeny, half of the males are Bw^a, while the other half will (1) die if a recessive lethal has been induced in the treated X chromosome, or (2) exhibit any new recessive visible mutations. Some results from the application of the ClB and Muller-5 techniques are summarized in Fig. 7.5.

The rate of mutation induction by an ionizing particle may be altered greatly by several types of cellular treatments. Oxygen is among the most important factors in the conversion of ionizing energy to biological change. X-ray induced chromosome breaks and mutations are decreased to 33 per cent by treatments in the absence of oxygen. Naturally anoxic cells, such as those at the core of certain cancers, are extremely resistant to X-irradiation. Cellular oxidative systems are so easily affected by a host of chemical and physical factors (antimetabolites, light and heat, oxidizing and reducing agents, enzymes and cofactors) that sensitivity to X-irradiation may vary greatly during the life of a single cell. In contrast to mutation rates induced by X and gamma rays, those induced by densely ionizing particles such as the neutron or proton are little affected by modifying treatments. In general these latter particles act directly and with greatly increased efficiency (about 8 to 1 on a per-ionization basis) over X rays.

Chemical and other nonionizing mutagens

Castor oil, penicillin, caffeine, oxygen, formaldehyde, ultraviolet light, and mustard gas have little in common except that they are all mutagens, substances having the ability to induce mutation. Many mutagens have the capacity to stop cell growth, and can thus, for example, halt growth of cancer, stop the sprouting of an onion, or keep a lawn from growing too vigorously. The mutagenic ability of the fabled mustard gas was demonstrated by Charlotte Auerbach and J. M. Robson in 1941. The ability of the mustards and related alkylating agents to kill cells, break chromosomes, and enhance mutation rates has been verified in a wide variety of organisms. Most of the nonionizing mutagens appear to act via direct chemical action within the chromosome. A few of these mutagens, like nitrous acid and ultraviolet light of 2,600 Å wave length, can be considered to act at certain fairly well defined locations in the DNA molecule. For example, nitrous acid specifically deaminates the nucleotide bases in DNA and so converts cytosine to uracil and guanine to xanthine.

One important class of mutagens includes the analogues of DNA's four nucleotide bases, A, G, T, and C (purines adenine and guanine, pyrimidines thymine and cytosine). Analogues like 5-bromouracil may masquerade chemically as essential bases and therefore may be incorporated directly into newly formed DNA molecules. The incorporation sets the stage for errors in the replication of DNA, leading to mutation. Mistakes in replication appear to be of two types: transitions, replacement of one purine by another or of one pyrimidine by another, and transversions, replacement of a purine by a pyrimidine and vice versa.

Randomness is characteristic of spontaneous and induced mutations, and of those breaks induced by most mutagens. Several chemical mutagens, however, do not induce chromosome breaks or mutations in the same proportions or locations as those that occur spontaneously. The alkaloid 8-ethoxycaffeine, for example, breaks the chromosomes at a high frequency in the vicinity of the nucleolus organizer, and maleic hydrazide produces high break frequencies in heterochromatin. The pyrimidine analogue 5-deoxyuridine induces unusually high rates of mutation in regions high in AT base pairs. It has been shown also that mutations induced by certain chemical mutagens can be induced to mutate back to wild type at a high frequency only with the mutagen originally used. It is unlikely that the geneticist of the future will be able to direct mutation of any gene he selects, but great strides are being made through chemical mutagenesis to permit greater selectivity in the mutation-induction process.

The application of both ionizing and nonionizing mutagens in agriculture has assumed many directions. The manner in which radiation-induced translocations were used in chromosome engineering by E. R. Sears was considered in Chapter 6. Many induced mutants have been put to use in plant breeding. The sterility and associated deleterious effects that accompany many mutations have urged the search for mutagenic treatments that enhance intragenic change in the absence of extragenic changes, a search that appears to offer reasonable promise of success. The ratio of intragenic to extragenic mutations is much higher for nonionizing mutagens such as ultraviolet light and the alkylating chemical ethyl methane sulfonate than for many other mutagens, including ionizing radiations.

Mutables

A major exception occurs to the rule that chromosomes replicate with regular precision. This exception is the genetic variegation (or mosaicism) that results from the action of mutable factors. Mutables have been known to the horticulturist since the early seventeenth century. Commercially important mutable varieties occur among the roses, carnations, tulips, zinnias, delphiniums, and camellias, to mention a few examples. Variegation occurs randomly through tissues, and in such a manner that each mutant sector can be traced back (more or less directly) to an initial cell in which the mutation occurred. Since genetic variegation may segregate as a monogenic trait, mutable factors are often referred to as mutable genes. The examples that follow will indicate some of the hazards in this simplification.

The first clue to the nature of high mutability was provided in studies of chromosome "stickiness" in corn by George W. Beadle and in *Drosophila* by A. H. Sturtevant. In lines showing stickiness, chromosome breaks occurred with high frequencies and often were accompanied by high mutation frequencies. It was proposed that stickiness involves some sort of agglutinative action at certain loci in the chromosomes. Subsequent studies of the effects of irradiation and chemical mutagens have indicated that stickiness may be induced rather readily by these mutagenic agents.

A second clue to the basis for mutables was provided by studies on the dotted or speckled seeds of corn by M. M. Rhoades. Rhoades showed that dotted (see Fig. 7.8) was a mutator factor that induced high frequencies of mutations at the A_1 locus in corn. A surprising result was that the mutations induced by dotted were reverse mutations, as from the recessive allele a_1, to the dominant allele A_1. In contrast, spontaneous and induced mutations at this locus always were from A_1 to a_1. The dotted effect also increased with increasing temperatures and with increasing numbers of dotted alleles in the triploid endosperm.

Fig. 7.8. Variegation in the aleurone layer of a corn kernel resulting from action of the mutable factor dotted.

A further clue in the unraveling of the mutable mystery came from totally unrelated genetic studies of position effects. When chromosome breaks occurred near the gene hairy, in *D. melanogaster,* the normal hairy allele lost its dominance, that is, the gene was suppressed. Similarly, when this gene was translocated to another position in the complement, its action often was suppressed. The suppression was removed whenever the hairy gene returned to its normal position. Similar position effects in *Drosophila* are often associated with variegation.

Chromosome breakage, mutator factors causing reverse mutations, and position-effect suppression were fit together as pieces in a jigsaw puzzle to explain genetic variegation through the classic studies of Barbara McClintock. Mutable or variegated patterns affecting a large number of gene loci in corn were studied by McClintock. In each case, dominant mutant sectors appeared on the background of a recessive phenotype. In one of her first series of 400 families, McClintock recovered variegated patterns involving 40 different loci! Cytological examination revealed that all mutable lines showed high frequencies of chromosome breaks at meiosis (recalling the observations of Beadle and Sturtevant). These breaks led to an assortment of translocations, deletions, inversions, and other cytological phenomena, and many of the associated genetic changes were lethal to the pollen or embryo. Plotting the location of these breaks, McClintock showed that in all cases they occurred in the same chromosome arms in which the mutating genes were located. McClintock observed on several occasions that one mutating locus had become stable while another locus in the same plant simultaneously became mutable. Cytological analysis of these events revealed that the chromosome breaks had switched simultaneously from the former mutating locus to the latter. It could be concluded, therefore, that the mutating genes themselves were not changing positions; instead, some type of mutation-inducing factor was changing position.

Studies of gene action following these transpositions of mutator factors provided a key to their unique nature. In each case of mutator transposition, the mutator acted as a suppressor of the gene nearby. As an example, when the mutator transposed itself to the short arm of chromosome 9, near the gene C (plant and seed color), color formation was suppressed to give the recessive, colorless phenotype (as if it had become, genotypically, cc). Following such a transposition sporadic mutants appeared in this line, of a type to be expected if c had mutated to C. Whenever mutators were transposed near a given dominant gene (e.g., X), three events occurred:

(1) Gene action of X was suppressed, mimicking the xx phenotype

(2) Chromosome breakage occurred at or near the locus X/x

(3) Sporadic mutation occurred, restoring the activity of the dominant X allele

Richard Goldschmidt viewed the suppression of gene action by mutator factors as a form of position effect comparable to that resulting from transposition of heterochromatin in *Drosophila*. The mutator's primary action was viewed as that of breaking the chromosome, often resulting in loss of the mutator itself. Losses of the mutator would result in removal of the suppression and the appearance of a "mutant" sector. Several different mutator suppressors have been studied in detail in corn, among them Ds (dissociator), Ac (activator), En (enhancer) and Mp (modulator). Similar mutator loci appear to occur in most ever-sporting material.

It is the rare genetic study that does not unearth as many puzzles as it solves. So it has been with mutables. For as yet unknown reasons, mutables mutate to other types of mutables. Some mutate early in the life of an individual, some late; some mutate at a high frequency, some at a low frequency; some mutators suppress gene action completely, some only partially; some have an additive or dosage effect, some do not. This apparent multiple allelism of mutable factors, and their frequent origin following the application of a mutagen such as irradiation, pose intriguing targets for further research.

References

Auerbach, Charlotte, *Mutation—An Introduction to Research on Mutagenesis.* Edinburgh: Oliver and Boyd, Ltd., 1962. 2 vols.

King, R. C., *Genetics.* New York: Oxford University Press, 1962. Chapter 13 is a most readable account of mutation, with an excellent bibliography.

Lea, D. E., *Actions of Radiation on Living Cells*. New York: Cambridge University Press, 1962. A classic.

Peters, J. A., ed., *Classic Papers in Genetics*. Englewood Cliffs, N.J.: Prentice-Hall, Inc., 1959. Note especially the papers by H. J. Muller (1922 and 1927), by A. H. Sturtevant (1925) on unequal crossing over, by Barbara McClintock (1950) on mutables, and by L. J. Stadler (1954).

Wolff, Sheldon, ed., *Radiation-induced Chromosome Aberrations*. New York: Columbia University Press, 1963. Among the more useful of the many reports from conferences dealing directly or indirectly with mutations.

Problems

7.1. Nonstaining lesions known as gaps appear frequently in irradiated chromosomes, and are often confused with true breaks. The following data are based on X-ray studies of the broad bean by S. H. Revell:

Dose	Gaps per 100 cells
20r	19
40r	38
60r	59
80r	79
100r	89

Calculate the regression coefficient b from these data using the formula:

$$b = \frac{\Sigma (DY) - \frac{(\Sigma D)(\Sigma Y)}{n}}{\Sigma D^2 - \frac{(\Sigma D)^2}{n}}$$

In the formula, D = dose, Y = gap frequency, and $n = 5$. Calculate the gap frequency expected at a dose of 200r from the formula $Y = bD$. Why do the data preclude use of formula relating Y to D^2 or to $D^{3/2}$?

7.2. The following translocation frequencies per 100 surviving offspring in *Drosophila* were obtained from irradiation of sperm cells (immature sperm were irradiated shortly after meiosis):

	.5 kr	1 kr	2 kr
Immature sperm	8	27	70
Mature sperm	1	7	13

Calculate k values from $Y = kD^2$ at .5 kr ($= 500r$), and the Y values expected at 1 kr and 2 kr. Compare with calculations based on $Y = kD^{3/2}$, and draw conclusions.

7.3. X-ray treatments of 1 kr applied after meiosis produce little sterility in male *Drosophila*, but induce dominant embryo lethals in over 96 per cent of their sperm. How might this principle be applied in the eradication of insects?

7.4. Approximately 50 cell divisions intervene per generation in man between fertilized egg and fertilized egg. Assuming 60,000 generations since the origin of man, and 10,000 genes per genome, calculate the number of intragenic mutations that would have occurred in the cell line from which you are derived on the basis of an average rate per gene of 10 mutations per billion cell divisions. (Answ.: 300)

Eight

Parasitism and Symbiosis

If the genetics of a single organism is intriguing, the genetics of two interacting organisms should be doubly so. This interaction often develops as a result of mutual benefits arising from the association. The bacteria in a cow's rumen and the wood-digesting fungi in a termite's gut illustrate this type of symbiotic or mutual relationship. The association of two organisms often arises, however, through benefits to only one member, a parasite or pest. Our immediate interest in agricultural genetics is to set the stage for the control of parasites and pests, and to put the symbionts to work. We are only beginning to recognize the complexity that this genetic interplay of organisms can assume.

Plant pests of plants

Disease-producing microorganisms known as pathogens make up the largest and most important group of plant pests. The bacteria, slime molds, and fungi are among the most important plant pathogens. Their combined effect on plants in the United States alone amounts to more than three billion dollars each year, a figure that would rise astronomically were it not for genetic resistance.

128

Complementary genic systems in host and parasite

The genetic variation of plant pathogens is best known to us from those fungi like *Neurospora* that can be grown easily in culture. Many of our most destructive plant pests, however, are obligate parasites that cannot survive apart from their plant host.

The first evidence for genic systems controlling disease resistance came from studies of obligate parasites, the rust fungi. In 1905, R. H. Biffen showed that the yellow stripe rust of wheat attacked only those strains carrying a particular dominant gene. The F_3 generation from crosses of resistant × susceptible wheat varieties segregated $\frac{1}{4}$ true-breeding susceptibles, $\frac{1}{2}$ segregating lines, and $\frac{1}{4}$ true-breeding resistants, indicating monogenic control of resistance. Many plant and animal pathologists were so skeptical of this contribution from the new scientific *enfant terrible,* genetics, that thirty years elapsed before a serious wedding of pathology and genetics was made.

Within a few years of Biffen's study, E. C. Stakman demonstrated that a rust species was separable into many genetically distinct physiological races. Each physiological race of rust parasitized certain varieties of wheat, but lacked the genetic ability to parasitize other varieties. By the use of different varieties of wheat, it was possible to fingerprint each race, as illustrated below for the bunt disease of wheat (S = susceptible, R = resistant):

Wheat variety	*Race of bunt*				
	T4	*T5*	*T10*	*L8*	*L9*
Martin	S	S	R	R	R
Hussar	R	S	R	S	R
Oro	R	R	R	R	S
Ridit	R	R	R	S	R

Each physiological race of bunt can be distinguished by the differing reactions of the 4 tester varieties of wheat. When different physiological races of a pathogen are crossed, monogenic segregations often occur for fingerprint patterns such as those above. The ability of a given race of rust to parasitize a given variety of wheat therefore depends on the genotypes of both the parasite and its host. The genic systems governing parasitic ability in the pest and resistance in the host are said to be complementary.

Gene-for-gene relationships

The genetics of host-parasite interactions is perhaps best known from the detailed studies by H. H. Flor of flax rust (Fig. 8.1). Genes for rust resistance were identified by testing the reaction of each flax variety to individual physiological races of the rust. The genes for

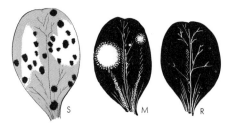

Fig. 8.1. Flax rust reactions of cotyledons. S = susceptible variety Bison inoculated with race 1 of the rust; R = resistant variety Dakota inoculated with race 1; M = leaf of Dakota showing pustules resulting from virulent mutations induced in race 1 by irradiation. Based on studies of E. A. Schwinghamer.

parasitism in the rust, in turn, were identified by testing on many host varieties. When rust races 16, 52, and 7 were tested on the varieties Bison and Williston Golden, the rusts infected only Bison (Fig. 8.2). The F_2 progeny of Bison × Williston Golden were grown, and the 3 races were again tested on these segregating families. A fourth of the F_2 plants were susceptible to race 16, $\frac{1}{4}$ to race 52, but only $\frac{1}{16}$ to race 7.

Flax line	Number of plants obtained	Rust reaction to race			Inferred genotype
		No. 16	No. 52	No. 7	
WILLISTON GOLDEN		S	S	S	*llmm*
BISON		R	R	R	*LLMM*
F_1		R	R	R	*LlMm*
F_2	92	R	R	R	*L–M–*
	26	S	R	R	*llM–*
	28	R	S	R	*L–mm*
	10	S	S	S	*llmm*
Inferred genotype		$v_L v_L V_M V_M$	$V_L V_L v_M v_M$	$v_L v_L v_M v_M$	

Fig. 8.2. Segregation for rust resistance in flax. Genotypes are inferred from these reactions for segregating F_2 progeny of flax, as well as for the three races of rust. Based on experiments of H. H. Flor.

The results in Fig. 8.2 appear deceptively simple at first. The data involving races 16 and 52 can be explained by assuming simply that two independent loci control resistance. These loci have been designated L/l, with the dominant allele conferring resistance to race 16, and M/m, the dominant allele conferring resistance to race 52. The results obtained with race 7, however, may seem puzzling. Only one-sixteenth of the F_2 plants were susceptible to this race; from their concurrent reactions to races 16 and 52, these plants are inferred to be genotypically *llmm*. It must be concluded that both alleles L and M confer resistance to race 7. Thus, race 7 is genetically different from races 16 and 52, combining the genetic inabilities of these races to parasitize flax having the L or M alleles. Flor designated the rust genotypes according to their virulence on different genotypes of flax. Race 16 was virulent on flax carrying the M gene, and was therefore designated $V_M V_M$. Race 52 was virulent on flax having the L gene for resistance and was designated $V_L V_L$; race 7 was virulent on neither the M or L bearing flax lines and was designated $v_M v_M v_L v_L$. At least 172 rust races (many arising from controlled crosses) have been shown to parasitize the variety Bison, and resistance has been found in other flax varieties to each of these. Multiple alleles at five different loci in flax govern resistance. The multiple alleles act independently in heterozygotes, inducing resistance to both the rust races inhibited by the two alleles independently.

Flor concluded that the genic systems of host and pathogen were complementary in flax rust, having a gene-for-gene relationship. The gene-for-gene concept states simply that for each resistant gene in a plant there is a specific and related gene for virulence in those pathogens to which the plant is susceptible. It is inferred that mutation and selection of host and pathogen have gone hand in hand, creating parallel genetic systems.

Comparatively few relationships of host and its plant pathogen have succumbed to gene-for-gene analyses. The parasitic relationship customarily is one in which resistance is a continuously varying character, conferred by a complex of polygenes. Geneticists working with many plant diseases agree that polygenic resistance to plant disease is preferable to monogenic resistance, since it is less likely to break down through the appearance of new races of the pathogen. As an example, resistance of beans to the anthracnose fungus is often conditioned by a single dominant gene. Such resistant genes, among the earliest reported, were once widely used in breeding work. However, new mutant anthracnose races that overcame the genetic resistance soon appeared, and breeders turned to polygenic sources of resistance. The proliferation of genetic races by sexually reproducing fungi like the anthracnose and the rusts often permits them to keep pace with the plant breeder. Monogenic resistance is thus quickly gained, but quickly lost. Other fungi undergo sexual reproduction only rarely, and new racial variation is uncommon in these species. In *Phytophthora infestans*, the fabled late blight of potatoes, only one compatibility group occurs throughout most of the world, precluding sexual recombination. As a result, no new races have been discovered during the century since the potato famine.

Animal pests of plants

Insects are the most devastating animal pests of plants. The genetic resistance of a plant to an insect pest may involve almost any physiological or morphological system. However, there are two critical points in the process of an insect's parasitism—its port of entry and the nutrition it seeks. The importance of the port of entry is evident with leafhoppers, insects that feed by sucking vascular tissues of broad-leaved plants, often transmitting viruses that also attack the plant. Genes that elongate the minute hairs on leaves of soybeans and alfalfa, for example, confer resistance to the leafhopper, since the pubescence holds the hoppers away from the cells they seek to puncture. Plants with rough pubescence are highly resistant, plants with appressed hairs are intermediate in resistance, and glabrous plants are susceptible. Morphological resistance of this type is often under the control of one or a few genes.

The nutrition sought by an animal pest provides the most important point in the genetic interaction of plant and parasite. A classic genetic study of this type involves the Hessian fly, *Phytophaga destructor* (see Fig. 8.3). In 1776, *P. destructor* arrived in the United States, apparently as a stowaway in a soldier's straw bedding. Like the Colorado potato beetle or the Japanese beetle, however, the connotation regarding the Hessian fly's home of origin is not wholly correct! The female Hessian fly oviposits on young wheat leaves, and the larvae fatten at the expense of the plant.

Fig. 8.3. Genetic resistance of wheat to Hessian fly attack. Left, homozygous susceptible plants; right, family segregating ¾ resistant, ¼ susceptible. Photograph courtesy of R. M. Caldwell.

Resistance to Hessian flies was found initially in the tetraploid wheat *Triticum durum*. This polygenic resistance was transferred to hexaploid bread wheats, and in 1942 the first resistant variety was released. Subsequent studies showed that resistance of the Californian variety, Dawson, was based on two dominant, nonlinked genes (H_1 and H_2). However, Dawson and other resistant California wheats were susceptible to Hessian flies in Indiana. Similarly, Indiana wheats were resistant only to their native Indiana flies, indicating genetic variation in both host and pest.

The close cooperation of entomologist and geneticist has succeeded in unraveling some of the genetics of the Hessian fly and its host. At least five loci in hexaploid wheat are associated with resistance, which is based on dominant alleles at four loci (H_1, H_2, H_3 and H_5) and on the recessive genotype at a fifth locus (h_4h_4). At least four genetic races of the insect have been identified, and may be distinguished by their virulence on the four varieties below (R = resistant, S = susceptible):

	Race of Hessian fly			
Wheat variety	*A*	*B*	*C*	*D*
Michigan Amber	S	S	S	S
W-38	R	S	R	S
Durum P.I.94587	R	R	S	S
Purdue 4217	R	R	R	R

A clue to the nature of Hessian fly resistance is provided by studies of larvae raised in artificial culture. When aqueous extracts of resistant plants are added to cultures, larval development is inhibited, suggesting that the resistance is biochemical and systemic. Larvae fed on resistant plant tissue die within a few days of feeding. The ability of plants to resist insect attack by biochemical inhibition is probably widespread. Most sucking or burrowing insects, for example, die if confined on any but a few species of plants.

Substances toxic to animals are common in plants. For example, pyrethrum (a type of chrysanthemum) is the source of universally applicable insecticides, the pyrethrins. An observant housewife in Yugoslavia first noted that dead insects accumulated near the fallen petals of her pyrethrum flowers. The pyrethrins comprise not one compound but an entire complex of related chemical compounds, each of which is toxic to insects. Chemists have devised many specific insecticides like DDT that are effective at relatively low concentrations when first released. Races of insects soon appear, however, that are resistant to many of these chemicals; for example, concentrations of DDT under 100 ppm. formerly would have killed most houseflies, while some strains now are unaffected by the pure chemical.

Evolution of resistance to a single toxic chemical thus appears to take place rapidly through the appearance of resistant mutants or recombinant genotypes. In contrast, the evolution of resistance occurs much more slowly when a combination of toxic agents is used. This appears to explain the continued effectiveness of pyrethrins (and resistance of pyrethrum) against a broad group of insects. This principle of the slow evolution of resistance to multiple toxins is also applied in medical treatments of tuberculosis bacteria and many other parasites.

Among the best-known animals that parasitize plants are the nematodes. Root-knot nematodes are known to infect the soft root tips of 1,700 plant species. These roundworms stimulate the formation of multinucleate giant cells in the root that house the enlarging worm. Injecting their stylets into neighboring cells, the nematodes feed from but rarely kill their tumorous host cells. Resistance to root knot is conferred by a single dominant gene in plants like the peach, pepper, and tobacco. Several dominant genes confer nematode resistance in lima beans. In contrast, resistance in garden beans is conferred by two loci, with resistance recessive. Resistance to the nematodes is generally physiological, the plant blocking the ability of the parasite to incite giant cell formation. Genetic races of nematodes with varietal specificities are found on some host species (e.g., alfalfa or clover), while they seem relatively rare on many other hosts. Parthenogenetic reproduction is common among the nematodes. This absence of sexual reproduction may account for the comparative lack of genetic variation in many nematodes.

Plant pests of animals

Bacteria are the most prominent among the plant pests of animals. Complete immunity to bacterial diseases apparently does not exist in either plants or animals. Given a debilitating environment and a massive dose of bacteria, even the most resistant animals succumb to bacterial invasion. Studies that have led to this conclusion could be cited for resistance to typhoid, piliformis, or tuberculosis bacteria in several animal species.

If immunity does not occur, how can one best assess the level of bacterial resistance in higher animals? It is out of the question to infect large herds of cattle, for example, if extensive deaths might occur. Several approaches promise rapid advance in these genetic studies. First, the immunochemical approach permits the detection of antibodies, incited in resistant animals to very small or subtle infections (as tuberculosis skin tests). In this way, for example, when young Berkshire swine, 91 per cent susceptible to brucellosis, were inoculated orally with small populations of *Brucella* bacteria, the first generation from selected resistant parents was only 27 per cent susceptible. Another approach to the question of inherited resistance in large animals is afforded by tissue cultures, which can be challenged by bacterial and viral pests in the laboratory.

The causative organisms of many diseases (those that cause the common cold of many animals, for example) are so cosmopolitan that their identification is often difficult. Exciting strides in these studies have been possible by the growth of germ-free animals. The use of germ-free animals offers a new look at long debated theories of the nature of diseases such as cancers, permitting distinction between genetic and pathogenic diseases, and between natural and acquired immunities. As an example, the growth of rats under germ-free conditions (see Fig. 8.4) immediately identifies tooth decay as a pathogenic condition, since germ-free rats are cavity free. Genetic changes in resistance to these decay-forming bacteria will be considered in the next chapter.

Resistance to bacteria is often conferred by genes governing immunological responses of parasitized cells. As an example, inbred mice strains have been bred with widely varying levels of resistance to infection by the typhoid bacterium (*Salmonella typhimurium*). J. W. Gowen found that the genetic level of resistance correlated well with the speed of immunological response to injections of heat-killed bacteria. Susceptible mice inbreds produced antibodies much more slowly when immunized than did resistant animals. It was suggested that genes for resistance controlled the rapidity with which a tissue could respond through antibody production to the challenge provided by the

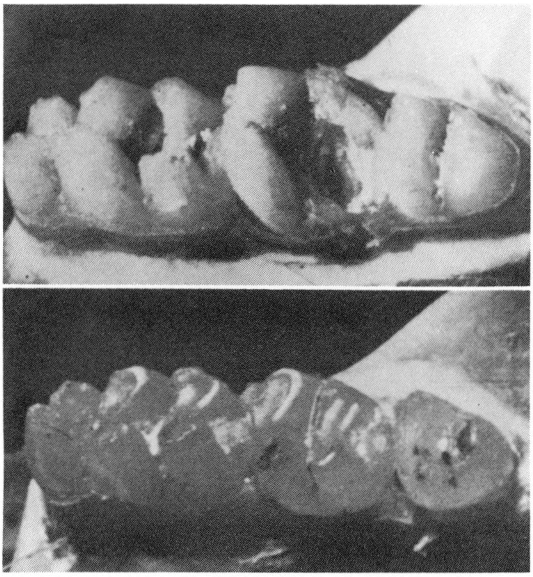

Fig. 8.4. Rat teeth. Above, a normal, decay-infected set of teeth; below, decay-free teeth of a rat grown under germ-free conditions. Photographs courtesy of R. F. Sognaes and F. J. Orland; from *Scientific American,* 197 (December, 1957), 112; reproduced by permission of the editors of *Scientific American.*

bacterium. In support of the theory, genetic strains of typhoid bacteria with different pathogenicities were obtained, and strains with low virulence were shown poor immunizers. Another bacterium of the genus *Salmonella* causes the insidious pullorum disease of poultry. The bacteria are deposited on the eggs as they are laid, infecting the young chicks. The Leghorn breeds are notably more resistant than other breeds, a resistance which is polygenic with a large dominance component and low heritability.

Resistance to bacterial invasion is often conferred by genes that bar the entrance of the parasite. A novel example of this type of genetic resistance is provided by the foulbrood bacterium, one of the worst parasites of bees. Infected bees carry the foulbrood bacteria into their hives. Once underway, infections are almost impossible to control. However, selection of resistant bees for a 3 year period was successful in trebling the survival from 25 per cent to 75 per cent under severe manual infections by foulbrood bacteria. When the nature of this resistance was sought, a rather unexpected condition was observed. The resistant bees were fully susceptible to the bacterium. However, they were simply more diligent than susceptible strains in their early detection of the disease, and in their efforts to clean infested cells and broods out of the hive. Busy bees better escaped bacterial infection— an example worthy of *Poor Richard's Almanack*.

Animal pests of animals

Nematodes, protozoans, and insects comprise animal pests of the greatest agricultural importance. Heritable variation in resistance has been observed in most animal pests of poultry and large animals. A classic case is that of the high degree of resistance to subtropical animal pests exhibited by the Zebu or "Brahman" type of cattle and breeds derived from it, such as the Santa Gertrudis. The resistance of Zebus to tick-borne protozoans and to tsetse fly–borne trypanosomes acts as a dominant trait in crosses. Each of these resistances is an example of klendusity (literally, barring the entrance). The tough protective skins of Zebu breeds repel flies bearing trypanosomes and ticks that carry parasitic protozoans and rickettsia-causing bacteria.

Resistance to animal parasites is commonly polygenic, with low heritability. Abundant examples may be found of animals with high resistance that, when weakened by malnutrition or disease, succumb to parasite populations having little influence on their more vigorous herdmates. The parasitic protozoa that cause coccidiosis in poultry, for example, are held in check by most chicks when small initial infections occur, as in the average clean henhouse. In order to discern genetic differences in susceptibility, artificial feedings of more

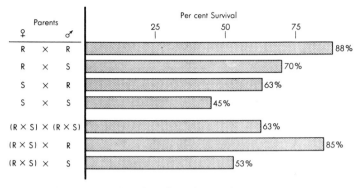

Fig. 8.5. Survival of chicks infested orally with coccidiosis protozoa. R = parents from highly resistant line; S = parents from susceptible line. Based on experiments of M. M. Rosenberg, J. E. Alicata, and A. L. Palafox.

than 100,000 protozoan oöcytes per baby chick are made. Using this method for several generations, a highly resistant line of White Leghorns was selected; intercrosses of resistant and susceptible chicks produced the results summarized in Fig. 8.5. Of the Leghorn chicks having two susceptible parents (S × S), less than half survived the massive inoculations of protozoans. In contrast, **88** per cent of the birds having two resistant parents (R × R) survived similar inoculations. While R × S and S × R hybrids were essentially intermediate to their parent lines, reciprocal crosses led to slightly different proportions of birds that succumbed to coccidiosis. Data from advanced generations confirmed the polygenic nature of inheritance and the absence of a measurable dominance effect (i.e., $V_G = V_A$).

Viruses

The viruses exist as obligate parasites in nearly all forms of life. It is the rare cigarette that lacks the best-known plant virus, TMV. Like most plant viruses, TMV (tobacco mosaic virus) codes its genetic information in the RNA's single helix, at the core of a protein-encased rod, some 150 Å in diameter and 3,000 Å in length. The RNA can be extracted and purified without destroying TMV's infectivity. The ability of TMV to mutate into new strains is legendary among geneticists. Differences in parasitic ability are common among the mutants, although alterations in host specificity are rare. The resistance of plants to TMV is often conferred (as it is in tobacco) by a single dominant gene (see Chapter 6). Resistance to TMV virus is not a form of klendusity (man is the most common vector), but involves biochemical reactions of tissues into which the virus is transmitted. Many natural plant constituents are poisonous if isolated and given in high concentrations to viruses or cellular pests. "Poisonous" plants carrying toxigenic substances are familiar to us all; common alkaloids such as nicotine, caffeine, and cocaine are not only suitable insecticides, but may inhibit growth of viruses, bacteria, and fungi as well.

Unlike TMV, the curly top virus of sugar beets is entirely dependent upon a single vector for transport. Curly top, carried by a leafhopper to beets, can survive for several weeks in blood of the leafhopper. The curly top virus cannot reproduce inside the insect nor in dormant plant tissues such as seeds. Resistance to curly top disease is conferred by genes that confer resistance to the leafhopper attack. The hopper is a phloem feeder that punctures only at those regions of high pH above vascular bundles on the leaf. Since the virus is injected into the phloem, it is able to spread rapidly, up to one meter per hour, throughout the plant. Mutants are common among the curly top viruses, many enlarging the host range or increasing the pathogenicity of the virus. A type of immunity appears in some plants once they have been infected with the same or closely allied strains of TMV or curly top viruses. More virulent strains, however, are able to overcome this induced immunity.

One of the worst diseases of poultry is variously known as avian leucosis or fowl paralysis. The causative organism is a virus that invades lymph tissues, creating a cancerous proliferation of the lymphocytes. The means by which the virus is transmitted is unknown, and even the most assiduous disinfestation of henhouses often fails to control the disease. Under natural infection, about 30 per cent of the chicks succumb to the virus. In one of the most convincing demonstrations of practical genetic control of disease, F. B. Hutt and R. K. Cole achieved rapid genetic advance through selection for resistance in the White Leghorn breed. Oral injections of the virus were administered to chicks for several generations. Following the selection regime, less than 5 per cent of the chicks succumbed to oral injections. The inheritance of the resistance to oral infection was polygenic. It could be demonstrated that the resistance was not a true immunity to the virus; when the virus was injected interperitoneally, almost 75 per cent of the birds succumbed. This inherited resistance promises ultimately to reduce greatly the financial losses caused by leucosis (losses that exceed $100,000,000 per year in the United States alone). Once again, although our genetic understanding leaves much to be desired, hard cash must be considered a convincing test of inherited superiority.

The immunological resistance of animals to virus attack may be either genetic (inborn) or induced. Immunological resistance created by childhood infections of measles, yellow fever, and smallpox is a familiar condition. That the measles virus greatly enhances chromosome breakage in infected children enforces us to admit the genetic complexities of such host-parasite relationships. The fact that resistance (of mice to yellow fever virus, for example) may be conferred by a single gene spurs interest in location and transfer of genetic resistance into plants and animals. On the other hand, the fact that immunity may be induced—in plants as well as animals—spurs studies of the mechanism of gene action and of immune reactions for immunological control of these viral parasites.

Symbiosis

The living together ("sym-biosis") of organisms is perhaps vastly more common than we recognize. In theory, two symbionts co-exist with certain benefits accruing to both partners. In practice, however, the partners take as much advantage of each other as possible without reaching actual antagonism (parasitism). It might be suspected that precise genetic relationships (e.g., gene for gene) would occur among symbionts. On the contrary, we find that these relationships, unlike those of parasites, are usually genetically haphazard.

A classical example of symbiosis occurs in the large first stomach or rumen of ruminant animals. Unchewed grass, etc., is attacked in the rumen of a healthy cow by roughly ten thousand trillion (10^{16}) bacteria and one hundred billion (10^{11}) protozoans—concentrations comparable to those of vigorous laboratory cultures. The microorganisms serve their host in an important way as symbionts; they live at the expense of, yet in the service of, their host. The enzymes of certain ruminant bacteria convert cellulose (straw, hay, wood chips) into carbohydrates that the animal can utilize for energy. In addition, many proteins and B-complex vitamins are available to the animal only through ruminant microorganism activity. In return, the cow's rumen provides a massive, warm, well-aerated and gently palpitated chamber, together with abundant food for the microbial guests. Several hundred races and even species of bacteria and protozoans enjoy this symbiotic ruminant life. It would be a splendid example of togetherness, except that the cow occasionally transfers the whole thing (250 pounds or more) on to the lethal acid milieu of the fourth stomach and starts afresh.

A more precise relationship of symbionts is evident in nearly all wood-eating termites, which contain symbiotic protozoans. The termites die of starvation within two weeks if their intestinal parasites, the protozoa, are selectively killed by high temperatures. The intestinal guests of termites provide the enzyme cellulase that catalyzes the digestion of cellulose. Therefore, the protozoa, and not the termites, eat the wood. A similarly specialized endosymbiotic relationship occurs in the drugstore beetle, which can only digest with the aid of an intestinal yeast, *Saccharomyces anobii*. After laying her eggs, the drugstore beetle carefully contaminates them with her life-giving yeast spores. Some other insects, notably the aphids, have special organs (mycetomes) that contain and transfer the vital microorganism to the eggs as they are laid. The genetic interrelationships of these symbionts are essentially unknown.

One of the most important, yet least understood, biochemical reactions in agriculture is that of nitrogen fixation. Through a unique sort of symbiosis, N_2 is reduced to ammonia in the roots of many plants by symbiotic bacteria of the genus *Rhizobium*—a reaction on which much of the world's agriculture indirectly depends. Neither the plant (usually a legume) nor the isolated rhizobium can by itself reduce N_2 to ammonia.

If *Rhizobium trifolii* is permitted to invade the root hairs of white clover, the root develops a prodigious overgrowth or nodule. The symbiotic relationship of bacterial and plant cells within this nodule somehow permits the fixation of nitrogen. When the same rhizobium is applied to the roots of a pea, however, no nodulation or nitrogen fixation occurs. Irradiation of the nodule-forming bacteria has produced some enlightening results (see Fig. 8.6). Mutants unable to fix nitrogen are common, as are mutants unable to produce nodules. Of greater interest are mutants that can parasitize new host species. Mutant strains of the clover bacterium that are able to nodulate in roots of peas and other species have been obtained from *R. trifolii*. These mutants have a host range comparable to *R. leguminosarum*, the common symbiont on peas and beans. However, the mutant strains of *R. trifolii* are unable to fix nitrogen in the pea roots, although they retain the ability to fix nitrogen in clover roots. Other mutation studies have revealed mutants with greatly increased effectiveness in fixing nitrogen. Two different genetic systems thus govern these two aspects of the symbiotic relationship, nodulation and N fixation. It is expected that combinations of mutants for host range and effectiveness may be made by sexual recombination or viral transduction to extend rhizobial symbiosis to many plant species.

The word *symbiosis* was coined in reference to the lichens. The combination of algae and fungi in the lichen is noted for its tenacity in the face of impressive environmental extremes; lichens live on snow, in geyser basins, and under conditions ranging from two inches to over four hundred inches of rainfall per year. The fungi parasitize the algae to compensate for their inability to conduct photosynthesis, while the algae evidently derive protection and nutritional advantage from the association. While the fungal species of lichens are not found separately in nature, all lichen algae apparently can exist satisfacto-

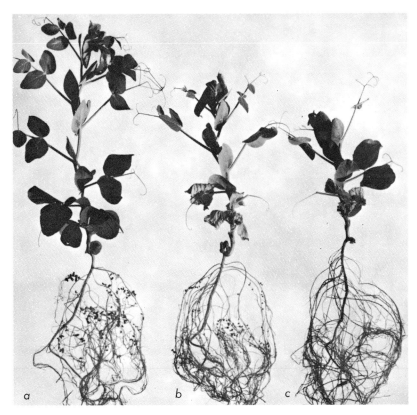

Fig. 8.6. Nodulation and nitrogen fixation on peas by *Rhizobium* species and their induced mutants. (*a*) Inoculated with normal symbiont, *R. leguminosarum,* showing full nodulation, full N fixation. (*b*) Inoculated with an induced mutant of *R. trifolii*—full nodulation, but no N fixation. (*c*) Inoculated with *R. trifolii*—no nodulation, no N fixation. Photograph courtesy of E. A. Schwinghamer.

rily on their own. The specificity of fungal species to lichen associations implies that they have evolved genetic systems similar to those of parasitic rust fungi. Gene-for-gene relationships can be expected to apply to some of these symbionts. In a similar way, fungi may associate symbiotically as mycorrhizae on roots of many plants, and green algae associate symbiotically with many coral polyps and other coelenterates, annelids, and molluscs. The nitrogen-containing wastes of coral, for example, are cleansed from the sea by symbiotic algae. The algae, in turn, provide carbohydrate foods to the coral-forming animals. Without this cleansing symbiosis, one great stagnant pond might cover most of our earth. It does not stretch our expectations too far to suggest that genetic studies of such symbionts will reveal both intriguing and valuable information for agricultural and industrial applications in the future.

References

Holton, C. S., ed., *Plant Pathology, Problems and Progress, 1908-1958.* Madison: University of Wisconsin Press, 1959. A thorough review of research in this field.

Hutt, F. B., *Genetic Resistance to Disease in Domestic Animals.* Ithaca: Cornell University Press, 1958. A refreshing look at the battle for disease control in animals.

U.S. Department of Agriculture, *Animal Diseases.* U.S.D.A. Yearbook of Agriculture, 1956.

———, *Plant Diseases.* U.S.D.A. Yearbook of Agriculture, 1953.

Problems

8.1. The streak virus of corn can be transmitted by some strains of the leafhopper, *Cicadulina mbila,* and not by others. When H. H. Storey crossed these strains, the following results were obtained:

(a) Transmitter ♀ × Nontransmitter ♂

F_1: 50% transmitter ♀ ♀
50% transmitter ♂ ♂
F_2: 50% transmitter ♀ ♀
25% transmitter ♂ ♂
25% nontransmitter ♂ ♂

(b) Nontransmitter ♀ × Transmitter ♂

F_1: 50% transmitter ♀ ♀
50% nontransmitter ♂ ♂

Interpret these results genetically.

8.2. Flax varieties Dakota, Cass, and Abyssinia each are homozygous for different resistance genes to flax rust race 6, but are susceptible to race 22. Races 6 and 22 were crossed by H. H. Flor, and the following results obtained when 67 F_2 lines were tested on the 3 flax varieties:

No. of F_2 lines	Dakota	Reaction on Cass	Abyssinia
37	R	R	R
12	R	S	R
9	R	R	S
9	S	R	R
5	S	S	R
4	R	S	S
1	S	R	S
0	S	S	S

Interpret these results genetically.

Genetic Advance Through Selection

*The greatest service which can be rendered to any
country is to add a useful plant to its culture.*
   —Thomas Jefferson

The ultimate goal of research in agricultural genetics is
to illuminate the way for genetic advance. Genetics has
had its most immediate application in the field of agricultural improvement. Perhaps genetic advance through
selection is most vivid, as Jefferson seems to have implied, when it adds a new plant or animal to the economy
of a nation or region. In one of the earliest genetics
textbooks, D. F. Jones[1] discussed the possibility of breeding hippopotamuses for meat production in warm,
swampy regions of the world. At first thought, hippopotamus improvement may seem a bit farfetched, if not
downright absurd. It would have seemed equally absurd
in 1925, however, had Jones predicted that geneticists
would be employed within two or three decades to breed
pine trees, honeybees, *Penicillium,* papayas, or rainbow
trout. Perhaps a crash program on hippopotamus genetics would still be unwise, but we may safely predict
great increase in genetic research on many other animals
and plants of untapped economic significance. The primary contribution of geneticists has not been to create
new cultigens, however, but to adapt existing ones to

[1] Donald F. Jones, *Genetics in Plant and Animal Improvement*
(Wiley, 1925), p. 11.

143

new areas or needs. Such adaptation reflects changes in gene frequencies that result from selection.

Selection

Natural vs. artificial selection

In the layman's sense, selection was a practiced art long before Darwin proposed his theory of natural selection. The Arab who stole sperm from a neighbor's prize stallion some seven hundred years ago was clearly on the right track. *Natural selection* was defined by Darwin as the preservation in nature of favorable variations and the destruction of those that are injurious. Genetic systems that preserve injurious variations (balanced lethals, for example) add some refinement to this concept. In this concluding chapter, we shall consider the subject of artificial selection applied by man, as contrasted with natural selection.

Artificial selection differs from natural selection in several important features; first, artificial selection is applied under a selected set of environmental conditions. In the selection of plants resistant to a given disease, for example, the breeder may inoculate each plant with the pathogen in a temperature-controlled greenhouse. An illustration of genetic advance through selection in a controlled environment is summarized in Fig. 9.1. Genetic variation for resistance to tooth decay bacteria (recall Fig. 8.4) is found in most animals, including the rat. When artificial selection for resistance to decay bacteria is practiced on rats fed the finely ground laboratory mash, little change occurs in levels of resistance. Tooth decay appears much earlier in rats fed on coarsely ground (rice-sized) feeds. When selection for resistance was practiced among rats fed coarsely ground feeds, resist-

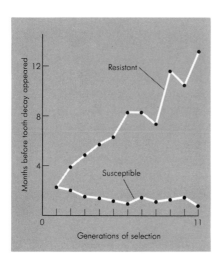

Fig. 9.1.   Resistance of rat teeth to bacterial decay. Selection was practiced among rats fed coarsely ground rations to increase resistance and to increase susceptibility through a period of eleven generations. Based on experiments of H. R. Hunt and C. A. Hoppert.

ance to tooth decay was increased sevenfold in eleven generations of selection. Selections of the most susceptible rats in each generation also led to a measurable increase in susceptibility. The choice of a proper environment, in this case a coarsely ground feed, thus permitted rapid genetic advance in the selection for decay resistance. What can you infer from these data about the genetics of resistance to caries-forming bacteria?

Under natural conditions, many genes influence the advantage that a given genotype may have over others, i.e., its selective advantage. In contrast, artificial selection confers a selective advantage only on certain genotypes that the breeder considers superior. Genotypes favored by natural selection are almost always more fit; that is, they have a greater ability to survive and reproduce. This is not always true for genotypes favored by artificial selection, many of which could not survive at all in nature.

Natural selection occurs normally under conditions of uncontrolled random matings involving large populations. In contrast, artificial selection occurs normally with controlled matings of a few selected individuals. In almost any segregating population of a cultigen, it is exceedingly simple to find undesirable features and to discard accordingly. Unless segregating populations are very large, it is impossible to find genotypes excelling in all desirable characters under selection. Therefore, the more demanding question in artificial selection is not "What can be discarded?" but rather "What should be saved for further breeding?" In large animal breeding, selection indexes are calculated that weigh the relative merits of an animal in many important traits. Animals chosen for further breeding will be exceptional in some traits and only mediocre in others, but will excel in some over-all fashion.

Genetic advance with monogenic traits

Selection acts to change gene frequencies; it does not create new genes. The changes in gene frequencies under selection may be illustrated most easily by assuming a monogenic model, with two alleles, A and a. The total frequency of these two alleles in any population is 100 per cent or 1. The frequency of the allele A can be represented by the probability value q. The frequency of a is therefore equal to $1 - q$. The frequencies of genotypes AA, Aa, and aa are obtained by expanding the binomial $[(q) + (1 - q)]^2$.

In the absence of selection and mutation, genotype frequencies remain constant from one generation to the next in large, randomly interbreeding populations. If selection is applied effectively, however, genotypic frequencies change; this is genetic advance or genetic gain.

Artificial selection involves the discarding of certain phenotypes. Let us assume that aa individuals in our monogenic model are of no value. In the event that heritability of this trait is 100 per cent, all *aa* individuals could be recognized and discarded each generation. Let us assume, however, that only a certain fraction, *s*, of the *aa* individuals can be recognized and discarded. The reproductive contribution of *aa* individuals (their "fitness") now can be symbolized by $1 - s$. The reproductive contributions of genotypes *Aa* and *AA*, from which no selection is made, will be equal to 1.

If we now consider the gametes contributed by the three genotypes to produce the following generation, these gametic frequencies will equal the products of the initial genotype frequencies and their reproductive contributions.

Genotypes	*AA*	*Aa*	*aa*
Initial frequencies	q^2	$2q(1-q)$	$(1-q)^2$
Reproductive contributions	1	1	$1-s$
Gamete frequencies	q^2	$2q(1-q)$	$(1-s)(1-q)^2$

Summing the gametic frequencies of the three genotypes, we obtain

$$q^2 + 2q(1-q) + (1-s)(1-q)^2$$

which reduces algebraically to

$$1 - s(1-q)^2$$

This total now is less than 1, since we are discarding each generation a proportion of *a* gametes equal to $s(1-q)^2$.

We may now ask what change selection will make in the frequency of the dominant allele *A*. All gametes obtained from individuals of the genotype *AA* will carry the *A* allele; this gamete frequency (see above) equals a fraction, q^2, of the total, $1 - s(1-q)^2$. Among gametes from *Aa* individuals, only $\frac{1}{2}$ will be *A*; thus, $\frac{1}{2}$ of $2q(1-q)$, or a frequency of $q(1-q)$ gametes from *Aa* individuals will be *A* (out of the total, $1 - s(1-q)^2$). When these expressions are summed, we obtain the frequency of allele *A* after selection:

$$\frac{q^2}{1 - s(1-q)^2} + \frac{q(1-q)}{1 - s(1-q)^2} = \frac{q}{1 - s(1-q)^2} \quad \text{(Eq. 9.1)}$$

This frequency can now be compared with that of allele *A* prior to selection, *q*. The change in frequency of *A* allele in one generation of selection may be referred to as Δq, and is obtained as follows:

$$\Delta q = q - \frac{q}{1 - s(1-q)^2} = \frac{q - sq(1-q)^2 - q}{1 - s(1-q)^2}$$

which reduces algebraically to

$$\frac{sq(1-q)^2}{1 - s(1-q)^2} \quad \text{(Eq. 9.2)}$$

Application of these formulas can be made in the following way. Let us assume that a poultry breeder wished to select for resistance to a given disease that is under monogenic control, with susceptibility recessive. If natural infections permit the breeder to distinguish only 50 per cent of the susceptible birds each generation, the value of s will be $\frac{1}{2}$. This value can be substituted in Eq. 9.2 above. We find that the change in frequency of the dominant allele conferring resistance (Δq) now depends on the initial frequency (q) of the A allele in the population. Several initial frequencies are assumed for the calculations presented in Fig. 9.2. The increase in allelic frequency, while numerically small, may be quite large when compared with the initial frequencies. It is to be noted particularly that this relative increase ($\Delta q/q$) is great when the initial frequency (q) is small, but becomes very small as q increases.

Initial frequency of allele A (q)	Change in frequency of allele A (Δq)	Relative change in frequency of allele A ($\Delta q/q$)
1%	0.96%	96%
10%	6.81%	68%
50%	7.14%	14%
90%	0.45%	0.5%
95%	0.12%	0.13%
99%	0.005%	0.005%

Fig. 9.2. Genetic advance through selection: Changes in the frequency of a dominant allele, A, in one generation when coefficient of selection (s) = 0.5.

When $s = 1$, i.e., when we can recognize and discard all aa individuals, Eq. 9.2 reduces to $q(1-q)^2/1-(1-q)^2$. When $q = 50$ per cent, for example, $\Delta q/q$ is 33 per cent (versus 14 per cent when $s = \frac{1}{2}$), showing that the relative advance under selection increases greatly as s increases. This relative advance becomes much less, however, as the initial frequency of A increases. When A alleles occur in a frequency of 99 per cent, for example, one generation of discarding aa segregants will increase this frequency by a mere .01 per cent. For this reason, selection for the elimination of a recessive gene from large interbreeding populations (e.g., man) is essentially impossible. Why might this not be true of small populations, or where inbreeding can be practiced?

Genetic advance with polygenic traits

Metrical traits governed by many genes are those most frequently involved in questions of genetic advance through artificial selection. We must use entirely different formulas to estimate genetic responses to selection with polygenic traits. Genetic advance through selection with metrical traits depends primarily on additive genetic variance. Stating this in another way, the rate of genetic advance under selection depends on the heritability and phenotypic variability of the trait under selection. This is formulated algebraically as follows:

$$\text{Genetic advance through selection} = iH\sqrt{V_P} \qquad \text{(Eq. 9.3)}$$

In this equation, the values H and V_P are those we have encountered previously for heritability (V_G/V_P) and phenotypic variance, respectively. The value i reflects the selection intensity, the percentage of a population permitted to reproduce. It is related to, and may be calculated from s (selection coefficient) under certain conditions. For metrical traits governed by many genes, the contribution of each allele to phenotype is relatively small. Under this circumstance, i and s become independent of gene frequencies (q), and these frequencies no longer appear in our formulas for genetic advance. The value i is expressed in units of phenotypic standard deviation $(\sqrt{V_P})$, and is known also as a standardized selection differential. Representative i values for selection in a population of 100 individuals are:

Per cent selected	90	50	20	10	5	1
i	0.2	0.8	1.4	1.7	2.1	2.5

Complete tables of i may be found in advanced treatises on selection.

The use of Eq. 9.3 may be illustrated with data obtained from a study of egg weights in poultry. The heritability of egg weights in the study was found to be 50 per cent, or 0.5. Phenotypic variance of the flocks studied was 2.59 ounces per dozen eggs, and the standard deviation $(\sqrt{V_P})$ therefore was 1.61 ounces. If we assume a selection intensity of 10 per cent in a flock of 100 birds, i would be equal to 1.7. The genetic advance in egg weights per generation with this selection intensity would equal $(1.7)(0.5)(1.61)$, or 1.37 ounces per dozen eggs. A dozen "large" eggs should weigh at least 24 ounces, by definition. Dividing 1.37 ounces by 24, we find that the expected genetic advance through selection in one generation would amount to about 6 per cent, a most satisfactory achievement in a trait of this commercial value. Similar calculations of the rates of genetic advance for egg production lead to disappointing genetic gains of less than 1 per cent per generation. This largely reflects the low heritability (around 20 per cent) of egg production (see Chapter 1). These calculations reflect long known facts that breeding for large egg size is more successful than breeding for increased egg production.

The poultry breeder reaches an impasse common to many genetic studies when he tries to put together egg size and egg production by selecting hens that lay many large eggs. This arises from the fact that egg weights and egg production are negatively correlated; as one goes up, the other goes down! As genetic advance is achieved for egg size, egg productivity tends to fall off, a fact more easily understood from the hen's viewpoint than from the statistician's. Thus, genetic advance under selection often is positive for one trait, and simultaneously negative for another. The correlation of two or more traits undergoing simultaneous selection is a fascinating subject that is left to your advanced study of the art of selection.

To these theoretical considerations of selection advance may be added the observation that selection is one of the great practiced arts. Few geneticists would disagree that something akin to intuition has made Burbanks out of people who could not have fathomed selection differentials or heritability coefficients.

Methods of selection

Genetic gains under selection depend ultimately on the accuracy with which the breeder can discern desirable genotypes. Since the heritability of metrical traits is often low, an individual's phenotype may be a poor indication of its genotype. The egg production of a single hen may be influenced so greatly by environment, for example, that selection of outstanding layers alone, with no reference to their pedigree or progeny, rarely results in genetic advance for this trait.

The method of selecting outstanding individuals on the basis of their own merit is known as individual selection. It is known also as mass selection when the selected individuals are bulked together en masse for subsequent matings. Individual selection is most effective with traits that are governed by one or a few genes, and which can be measured easily. It is rarely successful when heritability or phenotypic variations are low (recall our formula, genetic gain under selection $= i \, H\sqrt{V_P}$). Roguing, a form of individual selection practiced routinely in most breeding programs, involves the removal of offtypes from the interbreeding population.

An individual's genotype may be judged most critically for the typical metrical trait by considering (1) phenotypes of the individual and its siblings, or (2) phenotypes of the individual and its progeny. Family selection methods involve the choice or rejection of entire families of siblings that possess one or both parents in common. Full sibs have both parents in common, and thus have a genetic relationship of at least 50 per cent; i.e., they may be considered to hold 50 per cent of their segregating genes in common. Half-sibs have one parent in common, as the thousands of offspring from Monogram Rag Apple (Fig. 5.3), and their genetic relationship is at least 25 per cent. Clearly, the more closely related any two individuals are, the more reliable is the use of one to evaluate the other or of the average of both to evaluate either one. Similarly, family selection is most effective in conjunction with inbreeding, when degrees of genetic relationship are relatively high. Family and individual selections are often applied together in combined selection methods. In the simplest case, the best individuals from the best families are chosen.

Selection customarily involves, where feasible, a consideration of an individual's progeny. Progeny selection methods vary with the types of matings that can be made most economically with a given animal or crop. An outstanding tomato may be selected on the basis of performance of its self-pollinated progeny; an outstanding cabbage inbred may be selected on the basis of its progeny from crosses to another inbred (testcrosses); an outstanding bull, on the basis of progeny from crosses to its daughters (backcrosses). The magnitude of phenotypic variance, the heritability, and the degrees of genetic relationship must be considered in the selection of outstanding individuals on the basis of progeny performance.

Exploitation and exploration

Agricultural selection usually focuses on finding new genotypic combinations suited for traditional environments—e.g., croplands or corrals. Increasingly, however, selection practices are being retooled to find genotypic combinations that permit the exploitation of new environments. Agriculture has been driven slowly but surely from the choice farmlands of much of the world. Rooftop agriculture is already established and certain mutants of carrot roots and pine pollen, to cite two examples, promise economic production of food in tissue cultures. Developments in microbial agriculture depend greatly on the induction of mutations and selection of productive strains, already a practiced art with antibiotic-forming bacteria and fungi. Certain yeasts, often alluded to as the "oldest cultivated plants," produce high protein yields when cultured on the cellulose wastes of industrial plants. These proteins are high in lysine and are anything but palatable; mutant or recombinant types having low lysine proteins are greatly to be desired. Yeasts already contribute in an important way to our economy, through fermentation of breads and potables and through the production of Vitamin B12, lactase, invertase, and other proteins. An agriculture of the sea is not without its enthusiasts, not only for increased harvests of "seeded" fish and shellfish, but also for algae and other plants. There is every reason to believe that genetic advance for these new environments will be as great as it has been for the traditional environments in which selection has been practiced.

Each of these new environments poses the need for exploration to seek desirable germplasm, often in the form of resistance to pests, diseases, or environmental extremes. In this connection, the development of gene banks (of seeds, spores, or sperm) has become of increasing international concern. Thousands of varieties of corn, barley, rice, pepper, tomato, or wheat, to name a few, have been accumulated in central seedstock warehouses under the aegis of the U.S. Department of Agriculture and the Food and Agricultural Organization of the United Nations.

The disappearing beefsteak

Each day there are 150,000 new mouths to feed on our earth. At the time when genetics was born, a relatively modest population of 1.6 billion people inhabited the earth. Within one hundred years of genetics' birth, however, this population will have jumped by 275 per cent to a figure exceeding 6 billion. The world's food production must be trebled by A.D. 2000 if the present level of malnutrition (over 50 per cent of the world's people) is to be lowered at all.

The great thrill of exploring the unknown accompanies most scientific research. The thrill of creating new plants and animals is no less real to the experienced geneticist than the thrill that draws men into space or to the ocean depths. The student who chooses to explore genetic advance in agriculture will find the challenge of the unknown coupled in a most exciting way with service to the needs of man, generated by this exploding world population.

In 1960, a total of 12.5 acres of land existed for each person on the earth's surface. This acreage comprised: 1.10 A. under cultivation, 2.65 A. potentially cultivated, 2.50 A. too dry, 2.50 A. too cold, 2.50 A. too mountainous, 1.25 A. no soil. Exploitation of cultivated acreages could easily lead to doubled food production; exploitation of unused acreages, largely in the tropics, also promises great genetic advance. The initial investment for such programs clearly requires financial and technical assistance from highly developed nations.

Estimates have been made that man will be squeezed off the earth by his own population growth, even within the next century. While these estimates are doubtless overdrawn, it is certain that any curtailment of starvation below present levels in the next hundred years will demand some crash programs for genetic advance through selection.

Whether or not population growth is curtailed, we may safely predict that the agriculture of 2065 will be little similar to that of 1965. Gone or going will be many of those choice items that require more than their fair share of the earth's surface. The highly proteinaceous soybean, with annual yields exceeding 6 million kilocalories per acre (in the tropics) is mentioned as a likely successor to beef cattle (at less than 2 millon kilocalories per acre per year). Potatoes and cassava (30 million kilocalories) may ultimately succeed the soybeans. It will be unfortunate if geneticists learn all of DNA's secrets in this coming century, yet fail to make inroads on man's starvation. Indeed, it will be bad enough if the beefsteak disappears.

References

Falconer, D. S., *Introduction to Quantitative Genetics*. New York: The Ronald Press Company, 1960. Chapters 11, 12 and 13 contain an excellent treatment of selection theory.

Hayes, H. K., F. R. Immer, and D. C. Smith, *Methods of Plant Breeding*. New York: McGraw-Hill Book Company, 1955. Selection theory and practices in plant breeding are treated at length in this classic text.

Lerner, I. M., *The Genetic Basis of Selection*. New York: John Wiley & Sons, Inc., 1958. Required reading for advanced students of selection.

Lush, J. L., *Animal Breeding Plans*. Ames: Iowa State University Press, 1945. Selection theory and practices in animal breeding are treated at length in this classic text.

Problems

9.1. The absence of leaf markings in white clover (see Fig. 3.1) is a recessive homozygous condition, vv. About 16 per cent of the plants have this phenotype. What proportion of white clover plants are heterozygous for the recessive allele v? What proportion of the pollen grains produced by natural populations of white clover would carry this recessive allele?

9.2. Referring to Problem 9.1, if you were to eliminate all plants that lacked a leaf marking from an interbreeding population of white clover plants, what proportion of plants in the succeeding generation would lack leaf markings? What would be the $\Delta q/q$ under this selection program? under a program in which $s = 50$ per cent?

9.3. In Allard's data on flowering dates of wheat (Fig. 4.6), $V_P = 40.35$ days, and heritability $= 72$ per cent. If the breeder grows 500 wheat plants and saves seed from half of them, the intensity of selection equals 0.80; if he saves seed from 1 per cent of the plants, it equals 2.67. What would be the genetic advance under these two levels of selection pressure?

9.4. Assume that a papaya breeder is required to make a genetic advance in mean yield of at least 4 per cent per generation in order to justify his salary. The mean per-acre yield of papayas is 22 tons, and phenotypic variability is 1.21 tons per acre. Assuming a selection intensity of 2.0, what must heritability of fruit yield be in order for this selection program to be successful?

Index